Patricia Smith's

DOLL VALUES

Antique to Modern
Series IV

COLLECTOR BOOKS
A Division of Schroeder Publishing Co., Inc.

The current values in this book should be used only as a guide. They are not intended to set prices, which vary from one section of the country to another. Auction prices as well as dealer prices vary greatly and are affected by condition as well as demand. Neither the Author nor the Publisher assumes responsibility for any losses that might be incurred as a result of consulting this guide.

CREDITS

The author wishes to thank the following for their help and information. Each collector took their own photographs unless noted in parentheses.

Jayn Allen, Allin Collection (Dwight Smith), Jane Alton (Dwight Smith), Jackie Barker, Lilah Beck (Renie Culp), Shirley Bertrand (Dwight Smith), Sally Bethscheider, Kay Bransky, Joanna Brunken (Margaret Mandel), Sylvia Bryant, Alice Capps (Dwight Smith), Nancy Catlin, Nancy Cellitti, Pearl Clasby (Dwight Smith), Barbara Coker (Dwight Smith), Marlowe Cooper (Ralph Cooper), Jean Couch, Susan Crowsey, Renie Culp, Helen Draves (Dwight Smith), Barbara Earnshaw, Marie Ernst, Edith Evans (Carole Friend), Kathy Feagens (Dwight Smith), Joleen Flack, Eileen Flores, Margaret Gunnels (Dwight Smith), Phyllis Houston, Verna Humphrey (Sylvia Bryant), Earlene Johnston (Dwight Smith), Virignia Jones (Dwight Smith), Dorothy Judge, Kimport Dolls (Dwight Smith), Catherine Koelz (Dwight Smith), Angie Landers (Dwight Smith), Nancy Lucas, Linda Lucksinger (John Lucksinger), Margaret Mandel, Zoura Martenez, Jeannie Mauldin, Billie & Marianne McCabe (Dwight Smith), Marge Meisinger (Dwight Smith), Shirley Merrill (Brent Merrill), Mrs. Frank Miller, Wendi Miller, Rose Mills (Theresa Barklage), Jay Minter (Dwight Smith), Kay Moran, Louise Nixon, Beth & Carole Noi, Mrs. Nolte (Dwight Smith), Shirley Pascuzzi, Penner Collection (Dwight Smith), Penny Pendlebury (Chuck Pendleberry), Marcia Piecewicz, Evelyn Samec, June Schultz, Mary Sena, Betty Shelley, Jessie Smith (Brad Smith), Bonnie Stwert (Leslie Stwert), Ruby Stuart (Barbara Frazer), Sally Swan, Martha Sweeney, Mary Sweeney, Phyllis Teague, Pat Timmons, Mary Tollari, Treasure Trove, 19 Village Rd., Manhasset, N.Y. 11030, Turn of Century (Diane Hoffman) 1415 S. Broadway, Denver, CO 80210, Marjorie Uhl, Arlen Wacker, Erdeen Wagner (Carole Friend), Jane Walker, Kathy Walters (Dwight Smith), Freda Webster (Brent Merrill), Margaret Weeks (Dwight Smith), Ann Wencel, Mary Wheatly, Faith Wick, Mary Williams, Lita Wilson, Betty Wood (Carole Friend), Myrtle Worsham, and Yesterday's Child.

PRICES

The prices in this book are the retail prices of the dolls if bought from a dealer. Prices do change but doll prices are fairly stable in most areas. Once in awhile certain doll prices will shoot up due to avid interest in one area such as the early cloth dolls which have seen an sharp increase in prices over the past two years due to the supply of excellent examples being unable to meet the demand for them.

The **condition** of the doll is uppermost in pricing! An all original modern doll in excellent condition will bring top dollar and an all original antique doll in excellent mint condition will actually bring much higher than "top" dollar. A doll that is damaged or without original clothes or is soiled and dirty will bring far less than top dollar. The cost of doll repairs and clean up has soared and it is wise to judge the damage and estimate the cost of any repairs before you attempt to sell or buy a damaged doll.

An all original doll means original clothes and the original wig or rooted wig or rooted hair in excellent condition. This type of doll is what most price guides are based on. If the doll you are selling or buying is less than this, then you must discount from the book price to allow for condition.

It would not be fair to show "dealer" prices (what a dealer will pay for a doll) in a price guide or not to show the mint, excellent condition prices because all collectors need accurate prices for insurance reasons. An insurance company or a postal service must have some means to appraise a damaged doll for the insuree in case it is needed and the collector must have some means to judge their own collections to be able to purchase adequate amounts of insurance.

No one knows your collection better than yourself and in the end you must ask yourself, "Is the doll important enough to me to pay the asking price?" If so, you will buy the doll. If not, you will pass it by.

**Prices shown are for dolls that are all original and in excellent condition.
In some areas fair condition prices are also shown.**

ANTIQUE AND OLDER DOLL SECTION

ALL BISQUE-FRENCH

French all bisques are rather rare, with the majority of all bisques being German. Most French heads (socket) have a loop molded at base of the neck. The lower part of the socket head looks like an inverted bell and the doll is strung through the loop. Also they may have kid lined joints, tiny cork pates and most have thin arms and legs. The French all-bisque dolls have finely tinted bisque and are very well painted with outlined mouths, good painted lashes and feathered eyebrows. The majority of French have glass eyes, and very few have open mouths. They can be bare footed, have modeled on shoes/boots with painted stockings to the knees or the entire leg can be painted to give the effect of hip high stockings. If original or nicely dressed and in excellent condition with no chips or breaks the following are prices:

Swivel neck (socket head), molded shoes: 4½" – $650.00; 6" – $800.00.

Bare feet, swivel neck: 5½" – $675.00-725.00.

Jointed elbows: 5½" – $950.00.

Jointed elbows and knees: 5½" – $1,400.00-1,600.00.

S.F.B.J. Unis or other late French: 5" – $350.00; 7" – $450.00.

6½" French all bisque. Swivel neck, glass eyes, painted on stockings with maroon band around top and four-strap modeled on boots. Courtesy Kimport Dolls. 4½" – $650.00; 6½" – $800.00.

Swivel neck, glass eyes, open or closed mouth, nicely dressed or original and good wig. One-strap shoes and painted socks: 4″ – $200.00; 5″ – $225.00; 9″ – $675.00.
Swivel neck, painted eyes, open or closed mouths. One-strap shoes and painted socks. Nice wig and clothes: 4″ – $140.00; 5″ – $165.00; 7″ – $200.00; 9″ – $275.00.
One-piece body and head, glass eyes, open or closed mouth with good wig and nicely dressed: 4½″-5½″ – $125.00; 7″ – $275.00; 8″-9″ – $375.00; 11″ – $600.00.
One-piece body and head, painted eyes, open or closed mouth, with good wig and nicely dressed: 4½″-5½″ – $125.00; 7″ – $200.00; 8″-9″ – $425.00; 11″ – $485.00.

Molded on clothes, jointed at shoulders only or at shoulders and hips: 4½″ – $90.00; 5½″ – $125.00; 6″-7″ – $175.00.
With long stockings (to above knee), glass eyes, open or closed mouth: 5½″ – $375.00; 7½″ – $575.00.
Molded hair, one-piece body and head; painted-on shoes and socks, painted eyes: 5″ – $90.00; 6½″ – $175.00.
Flapper one-piece body and head, wig, painted eyes, painted on long stockings, thin limbs, one-strap painted shoes: 5″ – $250.00; 7″ – $350.00. Same with molded hair: 5″ – $250.00; 7″ – $350.00.
Pink bisque of 1920's and 1930's. Jointed shoulders and hips with painted features and molded hair or wig: 3″ – $40.00; 5″ – $55.00.

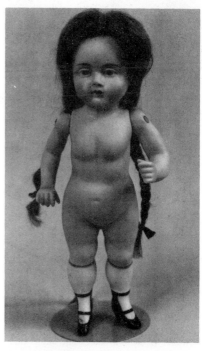

6½″ "Flapper" of 1920's. All bisque jointed at shoulders and hips only, open pate with original wig and painted features. Painted-on shoes and long yellow stockings. No marks, but made in Germany. May be original dress. (Author). 6½″ – $350.00.

9″ All bisque peg-jointed shoulders only. Molded eyelids, intaglio eyes and closed pouty mouth. Extremely well detailed body and legs. Painted-on socks and heeled boots. Unmarked. Made in Germany. (Author). 9″ – $225.00.

ALL BISQUE-GERMAN
ALL BISQUE-BABIES

7½" and 5" All bisque. Both have swivel jointed necks and also jointed at shoulders and hips. Both have open pates with wigs, sleep eyes and closed mouth. One has molded-on boots and other has shoes. Both made in Germany. Courtesy of Century Antiques. 5" # $225.00; 7½" # $425.00.

2" Tall all bisque jointed at hips and shoulders with painted-on socks and shoes, molded hair and painted features. All original as shown. Bare back rider on papier mache horse. Doll is wired through body into the horse's body. (Author. 2" with horse – $135.00; 2" without horse – $32.50.

ALL BISQUE-BABIES

All bisque babies were made in both Germany and Japan and dolls from either country can be excellent quality or poor quality. Prices are for excellent quality dolls with no chips or breaks, nicely dressed and clean.

Jointed neck, shoulders and hips. Can have glass or painted eyes, wigs or painted hair: 3½" – $100.00; 6" – $200.00.

Jointed shoulders and hips only, well painted features, free formed thumbs, molded bottles in hands, molded clothes, character faces: 3½" – $60.00; 6" – $145.00.

"Candy Babies". Generally poorly painted with high color bisque. Were given away at candy counters. 1920's: 2½" – $20.00; 4" – $35.00; 5"-6" – $65.00.

Japan babies: of poor to medium quality: 3½"-5" – $5.00-40.00. Very nice quality: 3½"-5" – $15.00-65.00.

Pink bisque baby: Jointed at shoulders and hips, painted features and hair, bent baby legs. 1920's-1930's: 2" – $60.00; 4" – $70.00.

All bisque dolls with character faces, stances or names were made in both Germany and Japan. The German dolls have finer bisque and painting of the features. Most will be jointed at shoulders, or shoulders and hips only, with very few being jointed also at the neck. They can be bare footed or have molded on shoes and socks. No chips or breaks and clean.

Baby Bo Kaye: 6¼" – $1,300.00.

Baby Bud, Germany: 5" – $185.00. Japan: 5" – $95.00.

Baby Darling: 5" – $65.00.

Baby Peggy Montgomery: 6" – $300.00.

Bonnie Babe: 5" – $825.00.

Bye-lo: Jointed neck, wig, glass eyes: 6" – $600.00. Molded hair, painted eyes, one-piece body and head: 5" – $375.00.

Campbell Kids, molded clothes: 4½" – $135.00.

Chin Chin by Heubach: 5" – $275.00.

Didi by Orsini: 6" – $1,250.00.

Googly, glass eyes: 6" – $500.00-600.00.

Googly, painted eyes: 6" – $325.00-425.00.

Googly, elbow and knee joints: 6" – $1,500.00.

Grumpy boy, Germany: 4" – $125.00.

Grumpy boy, Japan: 4" – $65.00.

Heubach, molded hair: 6½" – $250.00; molded ribbon: 6½" – $250.00; wigged: 7" – $285.00.

Heubach, Bunny Boy: 4½" – $225.00.

Little Imp, hoofed feet: 6½" – $265.00.

MIBS by Amberg: 3½" – $225.00.

Mimi by Orsini: 6" – $1,250.00.

Our Fairy: 8" – $1,250.00.

Our Mary: 4½" – $145.00.

Peek-a-Boo by Drayton: 4" – $225.00.

Peterkin: 9" – $385.00.

Peterkin, Tommy. Made for Horsman: 4" – $195.00.

Queue San Baby, various poses: 5" – $125.00.

Sonny by Averill: 5" – $625.00.

Wide Awake Doll, Germany: 7½" – $250.00.

Wide Awake Doll, Japan: 7½" – $95.00.

ALL BISQUE-NODDERS-JAPAN

"Knotters" are called "Nodders" and when their heads are touched, they "nod". The reason they are correctly called "Knotters" is due to the way they are strung, with the stringing tied in a knot through the head. They can also be made with cutouts on the bodies to take a tiny rod that comes out of the sides of the neck. Both styles were made in Japan and Germany.

Santa Claus: 6" – $125.00.

Teddy Bear: 6" – $125.00.

Other animals (rabbit, dog, etc.): 3½"-5" – $30.00-65.00.

Comic characters, Germany: 3½"-5" – $55.00-75.00.

Children/adults, made in Germany: 4½"-5½" – $55.00-75.00.

Japan/Nippon: 4½" – $25.00; 5½" – $35.00.

Sitting position, excellent quality (may be Orientals): 8" – $250.00.

All bisque dolls from Japan vary a great deal in quality. Jointed at shoulders (may have other joints); **Good quality** bisque, well painted: 3½" – $15.00-20.00; 5" – $25.00; 6"-7" – $45.00-65.00.

Marked Nippon with name (Baby Darling, etc.): 4" – $35.00; 6" – $80.00.

Child with molded clothes: 4½" – $20.00; 6" – $45.00.

Nodders (elastic strung): 3" – $15.00-20.00.

Comic Characters: (See comic all bisque section).

Occupied Japan: 3½" – $8.00; 5" – $12.00; 7" – $15.00.

Figurines (no joints): Children: 3" – $10.00-15.00; Teddy Bears: $20.00-45.00; Indians, Dutch, etc.: 2½" – $15.00; Santa Claus: $25.00; Adults: $25.00.

ALL BISQUE-COMIC CHARACTERS
ALL BISQUE

Mickey McQuire (copyright by Fontaine Fox, Germany): $65.00.
Herby #C82. Japan: $35.00; Nodder: $45.00.
Mr. Peanut, Japan: 4" – $35.00.
Johnny-Call for Phillip Morris, Germany: 5" – $65.00.
Mickey Mouse, Walt Disney: 5" – $60.00.
Mickey Mouse with musical instrument: $45.00.
Minnie Mouse, Walt Disney: 5" – $60.00.
Betty Boop. Fleischer Studios, Japan: 3½" – $25.00-35.00.
Betty Boop with musical insturment: 3½" – $25.00-35.00.
Baby Tarzan and Mother Gorilla: $35.00.
Orphan Annie: 3½" – $45.00; Nodder: $55.00.

Seven Dwarfs, 3½" – $30.00 each.
Popeye: 3" – $45.00.
Annie Rooney, Germany: 7" – $135.00.
Winnie Walker, Banner, Germany: 3½" – $65.00.
Skeezic: 3½" – $50.00.
Dick Tracy, Germany: 4" – $55.00.
Our Gang: 3½" Boys: $50.00 each; Girls: $60.00.
Moon Mullins and Kayo: 4" – $55.00.
Lady Plush Bottom, Germany: 4" – $45.00.
Mr. Bailey The Boss, Germany: 4" – $45.00.
Aunty Blossom, Germany: 3½" – $45.00.

ALL BISQUE

7" All bisque boy. Jointed at shoulders and hips with one-piece body and head. Deeply molded hair. Painted-on shoes and socks. Marks: Germany. Courtesy Gunnel Collection. 7" – $200.00.

5½" All bisque character. Jointed at hips and shoulders. Head molded slightly turned and down. Marks: 1414/Germany. Will also be found with: Germany/10950. Courtesy Helen Draves. 5½" – $145.00.

4" All bisque with molded-on clothes. Jointed at shoulders only with wire. Molded hair and bow. Painted-on shoes and socks. Will be found marked: Germany or Japan. Courtesy Helen Draves. 4" – $95.00.

4¾", 3¾", 3⅛" All bisque with all having molded, painted hair and features. All are jointed at shoulders only. All are bare footed and two have molded-on clothes. Left to right: Marked Germany, unmarked (ribbon molded in hair), Marked Nippon and "Chubby" that is made in Germany. Courtesy Sylvia Bryant. 4¾" – $85.00; 3¾" – $65.00; 3⅛" – $90.00; 3¾" – $165.00.

ALL BISQUE

5″ Wide eyed all bisque. Jointed at shoulders only. Glass eyes are set in (glued). Marks: Germany. Courtesy Gunnel Collection. 5″ – $65.00.

3″ Pink bisque bent-leg baby. Jointed shoulders and hips. Painted hair and features. Marks: Japan. Came in pink flannel blanket for 10¢ about 1930. Courtesy Phyllis Teague. 3″ – $65.00.

3½″ All bisque baby with bent limbs. Wire strung. Excellent painted feautures and molded hair. Made in Germany. Courtesy Gunnel Collection. 3½″ – $80.00.

5″ Pink bisque with painted features, painted-on red shoes and jointed at shoulders and hips. Has molded hair with loop for ribbon. Marks: Made in Japan. Courtesy Betty Wood. 5″ – $35.00.

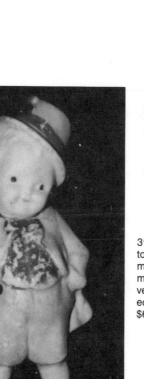

3″ All bisque nodder/knodder. Head sits in-to shoulders and is strung through hat. Head moves if touched. This "Irish" figure was made in Germany and Japan. The German version is much better quality. This one mark-ed: Japan. Courtesy Helen Draves. 3″ – $60.00.

2″ All bisque jointed only at shoulders, mold-ed hair and painted features. This particular mold was made in various sizes in Germany and was also produced in Japan. This one is unmarked. Courtesy Turn of Century An-tiques. 2″ – $18.00.

ALT, BECK & GOTTSCHALCK

Alt, Beck & Gottschalk produced porcelain from 1854, but it is not certain when they started to make doll heads. Their porcelain factory was located at Nauendorf, Thur, Germany. It is certain that they were producing dolls by 1893 when they displayed products at the Chicago Exhibition. This firm produced the "Bye-lo" and "Bonnie Babe" for the distributor, George Borgfeldt. The dolls will be marked:

along with a mold number.

Babies: After 1909. Open mouths, some pierced nostrils, bent leg, composition baby body, and wigged. Prices will be higher if on toddler body, or has flirty eyes. Clean & nicely dressed, no cracks or chips to head. 12″-14″ – $300.00; 17″ – $450.00; 21″ – $695.00; 25″ – $825.00.

Child: Open mouth, wigged, sleep or set eyes and on ball jointed composition body. No cracks, chips in head, clean and nicely dressed. 14″ – $265.00; 17″ – $350.00; 21″ – $425.00; 25″ – $525.00; 31″ – $1,100.00; 36″ – $1,700.00; 40″-42″ – $2,350.00.

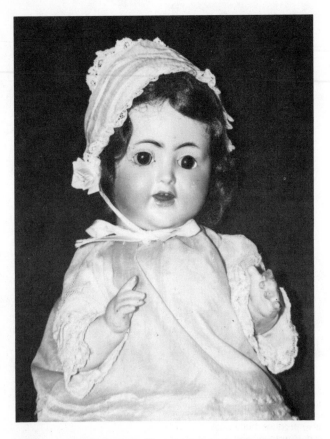

13″ Alt, Beck & Gottschalk. Bisque head on bent-limb baby body. Open mouth with two teeth. Sleep eyes. Marks: A.B.G./1361/48/Made in Germany/6. Courtesy Jay Minter. 13″ – $300.00.

AMBERG, LOUIS & SONS
Doll makers and importers

Prices for dolls in excellent condition, no cracks, chips, clean and nicely dressed.

Baby Peggy (Montgomery): 1924. Will be marked with the year and LA&S NY/Germany and a mold number. Closed mouth.

Socket head. Mold number 973 or 972: 18" – $2,800.00; 22" – $3,200.00.

Shoulder head. Mold number 983 or 982: 18" – $2,800.00; 22" – $3,200.00.

All bisque, smiling closed mouth, molded hair with full bangs and "Dutch" bob hairdo. One piece body and head, and painted-on "Mary Jane" shoes and socks: 3" – $265.00; 6" – $450.00.

Composition head and limbs with cloth body, eyes are painted and has closed smiling mouth. Hair is molded: 12" – $295.00; 16" – $400.00.

Charlie Chaplin: 1915-1920's. Portrait head of composition with painted features, composition hands and cloth body and legs. Black suit and white shirt. Cloth tag on sleeve or inside seam of coat. 13"-14" – $300.00.

New Born Babe: Bisque head with cloth bodies and can have celluloid, composition or rubber hands. Lightly painted hair, sleep eyes and closed mouth with protruding upper lip. 1914 and re-issued in 1924. Marks: L.A. & S. 1914/G45520 Germany. Also: L. Amberg and Son/886. Some will have "heads copyrighted by Louis Amberg". 9"-10" – $300.00; 14" – $500.00; 18" – $850.00.

New Born Babe: Open mouth version. Marks: L.A. & S. 371: 9"-10" – $245.00; 14 – $425.00.

Mibs: Marks: L.A. & S. 1921/Germany. Can have two different paper labels with one reading: Amberg Dolls/Please Love Me/I'm Mibs, and some without the Amberg Dolls. Molded hair with long strand down center of forehead.

All bisque: One-piece body and head, jointed at the shoulders and hips: 3" – $225.00; 6" – $400.00.

Composition: Composition head and limbs with painted-on shoes and socks. Cloth body. Painted blue eyes: 12" – $295.00; 16"-17" – $400.00.

Sue (or Edwina): All composition with painted features and molded hair with waist that swivels on a large ball attached to torso. Jointed shoulders, neck and hips. Molded hair has side part with swirl bangs across forehead. Painted brown eyes. Marks: Amberg/ Pat. Pend./L.A.&S. 1928. 14" – $265.00.

Twist bodies (Tiny Tots): All composition with swivel waist made from large ball attached to torso. Boy or girl with molded hair and painted features. Mark has attached tag on clothes: An Amberg Doll/Body Twist/Pat. Pend #32018: 7½"-8½" – $145.00.

Vanta Baby: Marks: Vanta Baby-Amberg. Composition head and limbs with fat legs. Cloth body, spring strung, sleep eyes, open/closed mouth with two teeth. Made to advertise Vanta baby garments. 18" – $165.00.

Vanta Baby: Same as above but with bisque head: 18" – $625.00.

20" "Baby Peggy" by Louis Amberg. Bisque shoulder head. Mark: L.A.& Son/982. Kid body with bisque lower arms. Courtesy Kimport Dolls. 20" – $3,000.00.

AMBERG, LOUIS & SONS

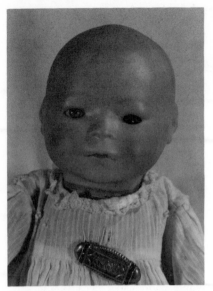

15" "New Born Babe" with cloth body, bisque head and celluloid hands. Sleep eyes. Mark: L.A.&S. 1914 G45520 Germany. 15" – $565.00.

14" "Sue" (or Edwina). All composition with turn and twist waist. Large ball in top of torso fits into chest. Jointed at shoulders, neck and hips. All composition with molded hair and painted brown eyes. Courtesy Sally Swain. 14" – $265.00.

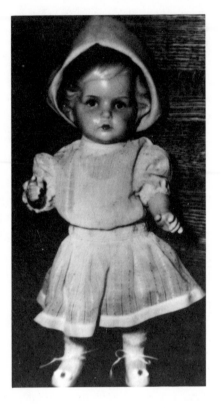

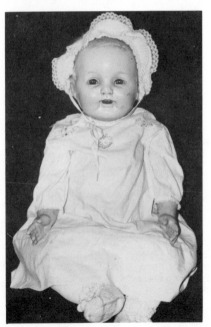

24" "Vanta Baby". Cloth and composition, sleep eyes, open/closed mouth with two painted upper teeth. Spring strung. Advertising doll for Vanta baby garments. Marks: Vanta Baby/Amberg. 1927. (Author). 24" – $235.00.

Prices are for dolls in excellent condition, no chips or cracks, clean and nicely dressed.

Armand Marseille made the majority of their dolls after the 1880's and into the 1920's. Their factory was located in Koppelsdorf, Thur, Germany. The Armand Marseille dolls can be of excellent quality to very poor quality. The finer the bisque, which should be pale in color and not have a smeared look to it, artistically painted features, will bring the best prices. The mold number 370 means the doll is a shoulder head and the mold number 390 means it is a socket head.

#370: Kid body. 15″ – $200.00; 21″ – $300.00; 26″ – $400.00.

#390: Socket head. 10″ with crude five-piece body – $125.00; 10″ on good quality fully jointed body – $145.00; 14″ – $175.00; 16″ – $250.00; 18″ – $300.00; 22″ – $350.00; 24″ – $400.00; 26″ – $450.00; 28″ – $475.00; 32″ – $800.00; 36″ – $1,100.00; 38″ – $1,400.00; 42″ – $1,700.00.

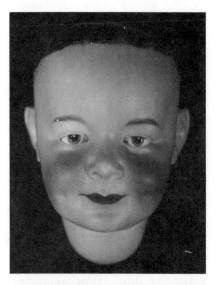

17″ Head circumference head marked: Made in Germany/A.7 M.. Feathered eyebrows, painted eyes, full closed mouth with deep dimples. Courtesy Catherine Koelz. 20″ – $1,800.00; 28″ – $2,600.00.

1890, 1894, 1897, 1914, etc.: Add $50.00 for composition body. 12″ – $250.00; 15″ – $325.00; 18″ – $400.00; 20″ – $465.00; 22″ – $500.00; 26″ – $550.00; 30″ – $700.00; 36″ – $1,100.00; 40″ – $1,600.00.

Baby Betty: 16″ – $425.00; 20″ – $545.00.

Floradora: 9″ – $165.00; 14″ – $225.00; 16″ – $300.00; 18″ – $350.00; 22″ – $400.00; 25″ – $525.00; 28″ – $575.00; 32″ – $725.00.

Queen Louise: 10″ – $185.00; 14″ – $350.00; 16″ – $375.00; 18″ – $400.00; 20″ – $450.00; 24″ – $500.00; 28″ – $650.00; 32″ – $800.00.

body, open mouths. Can be on composition bodies or cloth bodies with curved or straight cloth legs. Add $100.00-150.00 for toddler bodies.

Babies, newborn types: #341 with closed mouth or #351 with open mouth. "My Dream Baby" for Arranbee Doll Company. Some of these #351 babies will be marked: #345-Kiddie Joy or Our Pet: 6″-7″ – $165.00; 9″ – $200.00; 12″ – $275.00; 14″ – $350.00; 16″ – $450.00; 20″ – $600.00; 24″ – $795.00; 28″ – $900.00.

#341, #351, #345-Kiddie Joy or Our Pet with fired-in Black or Brown bisque: 6½″ – $200.00; 9″ – $265.00; 12″ – $425.00; 16″ – $525.00; 19″ – $700.00; 23″ – $900.00; 26″ – $1,100.00.

Baby Mold numbers - 326, 327, 329, 971, 985, 990, 992, 995, 996: Add $100.00-150.00 if on toddler body. 10″ – $250.00; 14″ – $325.00; 16″ – $395.00; 18″ – $450.00; 22″ – $525.00; 26″ – $750.00.

Character Babies: Add $100.00-150.00 if on toddler body.

Mold 233: 10″ – $300.00; 14″ – $450.00; 18″ – $600.00; 22″ – $900.00.

Mold 248: With open/closed mouth: 14″ – $1,350.00.

Mold 248 with open mouth: 14″ – $795.00

Mold 251: 14″ – $365.00; 16″ – $450.00.

Mold 328: 10″ – $265.00; 14″ – $350.00; 18″ – $500.00; 22″ – $700.00.

ARMAND MARSEILLE

Mold 352: 10″ – $265.00; 14″ – $350.00; 18″ – $500.00; 22″ – $700.00.

Mold 410: Some with retractable teeth: 14″ – $400.00.

Mold 518: 14″ – $450.00; 18″ – $550.00.

Mold 560A: 12″ – $400.00; 15″ – $475.00; 18″ – $550.00.

Mold 580: Has open/closed mouth: 16″ – $1,300.00.

Mold 590: Has open/closed mouth: 16″ – $1,300.00.

Baby Gloria: 14″ – $475.00; 18″ – $700.00; 24″ – $950.00.

Fany Baby: Mold number 231 along with incised "Fany". Can be on baby, toddler or ball-jointed body. With wig: 14″ – $4,000.00; 18″ – $5,200.00. With molded hair: 14″ – $5,000.00; 18″ – $5,800.00.

Character Child: They may have wigs or have molded hair, glass eyes or intaglio painted eyes and some will have fully closed mouths while others have open/closed mouths:

Mold 360: 14″ – $375.00; 18″ – $625.00.

Mold 372 Kiddie Joy: 14″ – $525.00; 17″ – $825.00.

Mold 400: 14″ – $2,200.00; 17″ – $2,600.00.

Mold 500: 10″ – $300.00; 16″ – $485.00; 20″ – $725.00.

Mold 550: 10″ – $495.00; 16″ – $895.00; 20″ – $1,300.00.

Mold 600: 10″ – $700.00; 16″ – $1,500.00; 20″ – $1,900.00.

Mold 700: 10″ – $700.00; 16″ – $1,500.00.

Mold 800: 16″ – $800.00; 20″ – $1,900.00.

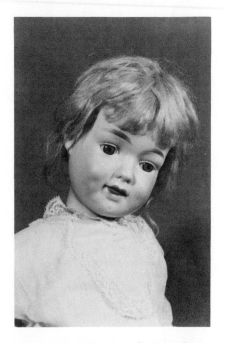

18″ Marked: 590/A 5 M/ Germany Drgm. Open/closed mouth, original wig and on five-piece bent limb baby body. Will also be found on fully jointed composition bodies. Courtesy Kimport Dolls. 18″ – $1,495.00.

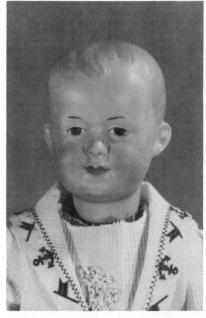

15″ Marked: A.M. 550. Molded hair, painted eyes and fully closed mouth. On fully jointed composition body. (Author). 15″ – $895.00.

Adult Lady Dolls: 1910-1920's. Adult face and have long thin jointed limbs with knee joints above knee.

Mold 400 and 401: 14" – $800.00; 16" – $1,300.00.

With painted bisque: 14" – $400.00; 16" – $700.00.

Googlies: Mid-1920's. Bisque head on composition body and marked with name and mold number 310:

Fired-in color: 9" – $900.00; 12" – $1,200.00.

Painted bisque: 9" – $385.00; 12" – $625.00.

During the early 1930's the Vogue Doll Co. dressed many of these "Just Me" dolls and their clothes will have the Vogue tag.

Mold 254, 320, 210 and others with intaglio eyes: 7" – $495.00; 12" – $1,100.00.

Mold 253, 254, 320, 210 with glass eyes; 14" – $1,200.00.

Mold 323 with glass eyes: Most often found mold. 7" – $625.00; 12" – $850.00.

23" Marked: Germany/Queen Louise. Bisque head with open mouth and on fully jointed composition body. Courtesy Kay Moran. 23" – $475.00.

13½" Marked: 1894/A M/2 Dep. Open mouth and sleep eyes. On fully jointed composition body. 13½" – $285.00.

31" Marked: A.M. Dep. on head. Has unusual modeling for an Armand Marseille and looks more like a Kestner mold. Large eyes, open mouth and feathered eyebrows. Ball-jointed composition body. Courtesy Turn of Century Antiques. 31" – $725.00.

ARMAND MARSEILLE

16″ Marked: Alma 6-0 by Armand Marseille. Kid body with bisque lower arms. Open mouth. Courtesy Kay Moran. 16″ – $300.00.

25″ Marked: Armand Marseille/Germany/990/A.13 M. On five-piece bent leg baby body, sleep eyes and open mouth with two upper teeth. Courtesy Jessie Smith. 25″ – $750.00-850.00.

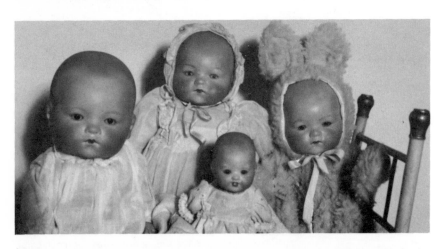

13″, 11″ & 10″ Head circumference "My Dream Baby" made by Armand Marseille for Arranbee Dolls. Mold number 341 has a closed mouth and 351 has an open mouth. Will be found on cloth bodies with composition, celluloid or rubber hands. Courtesy Turn of Century Antiques. 10″ – $250.00; 11″ – $275.00; 13″ – $345.00.

ARMAND MARSEILLE

17½" Marked: A 7 M/980/DRGM. Open mouth with sleep eyes and on five-piece bent limb baby body. Courtesy Yesterday's Child. 17½" – $450.00.

Both dolls are marked: Made in Germany/A 12/0 M. Both are 6½" tall and have fully jointed bodies. Courtesy of Turn of Century Antiques. 6½"-7" – $185.00.

ARMAND MARSEILLE
ARNOLD, OSCAR

Right: 11" Painted bisque marked: 390 A.M. Has open mouth and is all original. Left has closed mouth, is painted bisque and dressed original. Courtesy Turn of Century Antiques. 11" (right) – $145.00; 11" (left) – $195.00.

15½" Shoulder head with kid body and bisque lower arms. Open mouth and set eyes. One stroke eyebrows. Ca. 1888. Arnold mark, plus 200/8. Courtesy Kathy Walters. The Max Oscar Arnold dolls were made from 1878 to late 1920's. The factory was located in Neustadt near Coburg, Germany. Marks: MOA. 15½" – $185.00.

AVERILL, GEORGENE (MADAME HENDRON)

Georgene Averill started making dolls in 1913 and she used various names: Madame Hendren, Madame Georgene Dolls, Paul Averill Mfg. Co., Averill Mfg. Co., Georgene Novelties, Brophey Doll Co. in Canada. She also made dolls for George Borgfeldt. Prices are for dolls with no chips, cracks, are clean and nicely dressed.

Mama style dolls: Marks: Baby Georgene, Baby Hendren, etc. Composition and cloth: 15" - $115.00; 21" - $150.00.

Baby Yawn: Composition, yawn mouth and closed eyes: 17" - $200.00.

Body Twist: All composition, large ball-jointed waist: 14" - $265.00.

Cloth Dolls: Children, mask faces, yarn hair: 14" - $100.00.

Comic characters: 14" - $225.00.

Internationals: foreign costumes: 12" - $50.00; 22" - $100.00.

Two heads/Topsy & Eva: 10" - $85.00.

Dolly Dingle (for Grace Drayton): 11" - $265.00.

Fangel, Maude Tousey (designer) child: 12" - $300.00.

Dolly Record: Composition and cloth with record player in back: 26" - $435.00.

Indian, Sailor, Dutch, Cowboy, Black: Composition with yarn or molded hair, painted features and cloth body. Majority original clothes are felt: 14" - $125.00; 19" - $225.00.

Snookums: Composition/cloth. Character from "The Newlyweds" by George McManus. Smile face: 14" - $265.00.

Whistling Boy: Composition/cloth with bellows in legs: 14" - $125.00; Same but Black: 14" - $150.00.

21" "Baby Georgene" and so marked on head. Composition and cloth. All fingers curled under. 21" - $150.00.

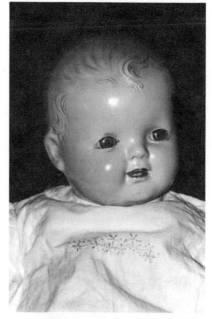

22" "Baby Hendren". Composition and cloth, open mouth with two upper and lower teeth. Marks: Baby Hendren. Courtesy Kathy Walters. 22" - $160.00.

BAHR & PROSCHILD
BEBE CHARMANT

Bahr and Proschild operated at Ohrdruf, Thur, Germany from 1871 until the late 1920's. By 1910 they were also making celluloid doll heads and parts. The marks from the company are:

Character baby: 1909 to end of production. Bent limb baby body, sleep eyes, wigged and open mouths. Allow $100.00-150.00 for toddler body. No cracks, chips or other damage and nicely dressed.

Mold 604, 624, 678, 585: 13" – $400.00; 16" – $500.00; 19" – $575.00; 25" – $950.00.

Mold 169: 12" – $425.00; 16" – $525.00; 20" – $625.00.

Character Child: Can be on fully jointed composition body or toddler body. Nicely dressed, no damage, chips or breaks.

Molded hair or wigged: 16" – $1,800.00; 20" – $2,600.00; 23" – $3,100.00.

Mold 2072. (Open/closed mouth): 16" – $2,400.00; 20" – $3,200.00.

18" with 12" head circumference character baby on five-piece bent limb baby body. Open mouth with two upper teeth. Marks: 678-8/ BP . Courtesy Jay Minter. 18" – $550.00.

12" "Bebe Charmant". Made in 1892 by Henri Pintel of Pinet & Godchaux. Montreuil, France. Crude papier mache body and legs. Slightly better quality papier mache arms. Bisque head with set eyes and closed mouth. All original clothes. Marks: H.P./1 on head. Stamped with name on underclothes. Courtesy Jay Minter. 12" – $1,500.00.

Stamp "Bebe Charmant" on underclothes of 12" doll.

So called "Belton" dolls are not marked or marked with only a number. They come on French style bodies and most have almost white bisque with a pink wash over the eyes and many have wide open/closed mouths with the area between the lips left white. "Belton" dolls have a concave flat top to the solid uncut head with one to three holes for stringing and plugging in wigs. These dolls differ from the "dome", "Bald" and "ball" heads that are German. The German heads are solid shaped and completely round on top and some may have one or two holes for stringing or wigs.

Prices for "Belton" dolls with French quality heads and bodies and with concave top to head with from one to three holes are: 10" – $995.00; 12" – $1.050.00; 15" – $1,400.00; 18" – $1,900.00; 20" – $2,000.00; 23" – $2,400.00; 26" – $2,900.00.

20" "Belton-type" with concave head and two string holes. Wide open/closed mouth with area between lips left white. Straight wrist French body. Unmarked. 20" – $2,000.00.

12" "Belton type" with wide open/closed mouth and area between lips left white. Pierced ears and on jointed French composition body. Courtesy Jay Minter. 12" – $1,050.00.

22" "Belton-type" with concave head and stringing holes. Pierced ears and has wide open/closed mouth with lip color throughout. Marks: 204, on head. On French body that is fully jointed. Courtesy Jay Minter. 22" – $2,200.00.

BELTON-TYPE
BERGMANN, C.M.

6½" "Belton type" that is concave and has two stringing holes. Marks: 60/F-O. Cardboard body with papier mache limbs, painted-on boots. Original costume of Russia. Doll came without wig and wears hat. Courtesy Shirley Pascuzzi. 6½" – $400.00.

The Charles M. Bergmann firm operated from 1889 at both Walterhausen and Friedrichroda, Germany. He made dolls in kid, as well as, ball jointed bodies with the bisque heads being made for him by such companies as Simon & Halbig, Armand Marseille, Kestner and others.

Marks on Bergmann, dolls very often carry the full name C.M. Bergmann, but at times will have the name or initials of the maker of the head, along with his initials C.M.B.

Child Doll: On fully jointed body and with open mouth. 18" – $325.00; 21" – $425.00; 24" – $475.00; 27" – $650.00; 30" – $725.00; 34" – $1,200.00; 40" – $1,900.00.

Character Baby: Socket head on five-piece bent limb baby body. Open mouth. 12" – $395.00; 16" – $495.00; 20" – $650.00.

Lady Doll: Adult style body with long thin limbs of the "flapper" type: 14" – $850.00; 17" – $1,200.00; 21" – $1,600.00.

18" Marks: C.M. Bergmann/Walterhausen/-Germany/1916/3. Sleep eyes with real hair lashes, open mouth and feathered eyebrows. 18" – $325.00.

22" Marked: C.M.Bergmann/Simon & Halbig/10½. Open mouth, molded, feathered eyebrows and real hair lashes. Courtesy Jay Minter. 22" – $475.00.

BERGMANN, C.M.

16″ Marked: C.M.Bergmann on head. Sleep eyes and open mouth. On five-piece bent limb baby body. Courtesy Yesterday's Child. 16″ – $495.00.

B.F.

The B.F. dolls were made by Ferte as Bebe Ferte, but are also referred to as Bebe Francaise by Jumeau. They have closed mouths and are on jointed composition bodies with most having straight wrists. 14″ – $2,300.00; 17″ – $2,800.00; 21″ – $3,000.00; 25″ – $3,500.00.

20″ Marked: B.F. on head. Heavily feathered eyebrows, closed mouth and pierced ears. On jointed body with straight wrists. 20″ – $2,800.00.

BLACK OR BROWN DOLLS

Black or Brown dolls can have fired-in color or painted bisque; they can range from pure black to very light tan. The quality of these dolls differs greatly and prices are based on excellent quality of color. These dolls were also made by both the German and the French.

Armand Marseille 341 or 351: 14" – $475.00; 18" – $700.00.

Armand Marseille 390N: 16" – $425.00; 21" – $650.00.

Armand Marseille 518: 16" – $650.00; 20" – $725.00.

Armand Marseille 1894: 14" – $450.00; 17" – $600.00.

Bru Jne: 17" – $12,500.00; 21" – $14,550.00.

Bru, Circle Dot or Brevete: 17" – $12,500.00.

French, unmarked. Closed mouth: 14" – $1,600.00; 18" – $2,000.00.

French, unmarked. Open mouth: 12" – $475.00; 16" – $1,000.00; 21" – $1,600.00.

German, unmarked. Closed mouth: 6½" – $285.00; 9" – $495.00; 14" – $600.00.

German, unmarked. Open mouth: 12" – $325.00; 16" – $475.00; 19" – $700.00.

Hanna, Schoenau & Hoffmeister: 12" – $385.00; 16" – $495.00.

Heubach, Gebruder (Sunburst mark-7671): 8" – $800.00; 12" – $1,000.00.

Heubach, Gebruder (Sunburst mark) Boy, eyes to side: 11" – $1,000.00.

Heubach Kopplesdorf 399: 9" – $350.00; 12" – $400.00; 16" – $600.00.

Heubach Kopplesdorf 463: 10" – $550.00; 14" – $750.00.

Heubach Kopplesdorf 444: 10" – $365.00; 14" – $700.00.

Heubach Kopplesdorf 1900: 13" – $450.00; 16" – $600.00.

Jumeau. Open mouth: 12" – $1,600.00; 16" – $1,950.00; 21" – $2,400.00.

Jumeau. Closed mouth: 12" – $3,000.00; 16" – $4,000.00; 21" – $5,000.00.

Jumeau. Marked: E.J.: 12" – $3,400.00; 16" – $4,400.00.

K star R. 100: 16" – $1,000.00; 18" – $1,300.00.

K star R 116A: 16" – $2,400.00; 18" – $2,700.00.

K star R 126: 16" – $465.00; 18" – $650.00.

Kestner. Marked: 10" – $465.00; 14" – $595.00.

Recknagel. Marked: R.A.: 14" – $500.00; 20" – $1,400.00.

Schoenau & Hoffmeister 1909: 14" – $465.00; 17" – $525.00.

Scowling Indian: 10" – $325.00; 13" – $465.00.

Simon & Halbig. 1039: 14" – $495.00; 17" – $650.00.

Simon & Halbig. 1358: 14" – $3,100.00; 17" – $4,000.00.

S.F.B.J. Open mouth 301: 17" – $525.00.

Steiner, Jules. Open mouth: 14" – $2,400.00.

S & Q 251: 10" – $465.00; 14" – $595.00.

Unis 301 or 60: 12" – $265.00.

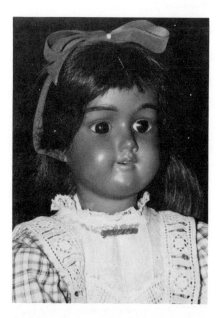

16" Brown bisque head, black sleep eyes, open mouth and brown ball jointed body. Marks: Made in Germany/Armand Marseille/390n/D.R.G.M. 246/a/A.2½ M. 16" – $425.00.

BLACK OR BROWN DOLLS

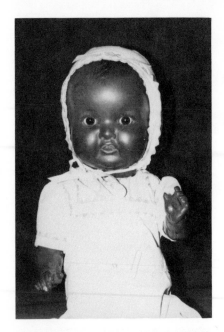

20″ Composition baby made after 1910. Marks: AM/Germany/518-6/k. Courtesy Jay Minter. 20″ – $725.00.

12″ Bisque head with sleep eyes, open mouth and on jointed brown body. Marks: S PB H/ 1909/4//0 Germany. Made by Schoenau and Hoffmeister. 12″ – $385.00.

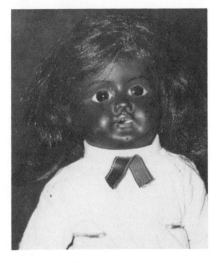

11½″ Russian brown bisque of 1930 using an old German mold. All original. Marks: *ЯЯ* . Courtesy Kimport Dolls. 11½″ – $325.00.

11″ Black doll by unknown maker. Bisque head, papier mache body and limbs. Marks: 12/0. Courtesy Kimport Dolls. 11″ – $300.00.

The "Bonnie Babe" was designed by Georgene Averill in 1926. The bisque heads were made in Germany by Alt, Beck & Gottschalck. The bodies are cloth and arms and legs of composition, or cloth body and legs. They are marked: Copy. by/George Averill/Germany and/or marked with a number 1005/3652. Open smiling mouth with two lower teeth. Measured by head circumference:12"-13" – $750.00; 14"-15" – $1,000.00. All bisque: 5" – $825.00. Celluloid head: Head circumference: 8"-9" – $300.00.

14½" Head circumference "Bonnie Babe". Bisque head with flange neck, open mouth with two lower teeth and cloth body with composition arms. Straight composition baby legs. Marks: Copy. by/Georgene Averill/-1005/3652/Germany. Costumed in owner's childhood clothes. Courtesy Margaret Mandel. 14½" – $1,000-1,200.00.

16" Stone bisque bonnet doll with poke bonnet and ties modeled as part of head. Courtesy Helen Draves. 16" – $375.00.

13" Bonnet head with molded blouse top with necklace. Cloth body with stone bisque lower arms. Courtesy Kimport Dolls. 13" – $375.00.

BONNET DOLLS

13″ Stone bisque bonnet head called "Jockey Cap". Cloth body with stone bisque limbs. Courtesy Kimport Dolls. 13″ – $375.00.

13″ Bonnet head with molded shoulder decoration. Cloth body and stone bisque lower arms. Courtesy Kimport Dolls. 13″ – $275.00.

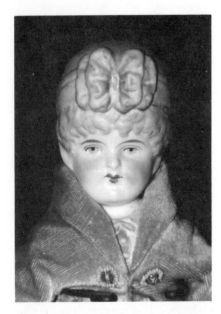

13″ Turban type bonnet doll of stone bisque. Modeled on shirt top. Courtesy Helen Draves. 13″ – $275.00.

12″ Bonnet head of stone bisque. Cloth body with china limbs. Courtesy Zoura Martinez. 12″ – $250.00.

6" Bonnet doll that is all bisque and jointed at shoulders only. Styled like the "Frozen Charlotte" dolls. Courtesy Helen Draves. 6" – $125.00.

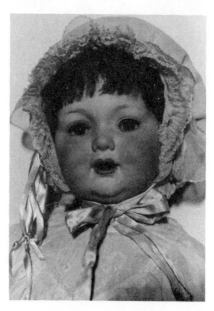

24" Bisque head with sleep eyes and open mouth. On fully jointed composition body. Marks: Germany/G.B. Made in Germany for George Borgfeldt who was an importer and distributor. 24" – $475.00.

15" Head circumference baby marked: G 327 B. Open mouth with two upper teeth. Real hair lashes and feathered eyebrows. Five piece bent limb baby body. George Borgfeldt was a distributor and importer and had many dolls made for him. This doll was made by the Armand Marseille using their 327 mold. Courtesy Turn of Century Antiques. 15" head – $900.00.

BOUDOIR DOLLS

In the 1920's some of the American makers of Boudoir-Bed dolls were Unique Novelty, Sterling Doll Co., American Stuffed Novelty Co., Fred K. Braiting, Charles Blomm, Inc., Gerling Toy Co. and many others. Very rarely is a doll of this type found with marks of makers.

Called "Flapper" or "Vamp" dolls due to the time period they were popular in, which was 1920's into early 1930's. Not all Boudoir dolls were expensive, nor even well made. The least expensive had composition heads and shoulder plates made in two pieces or with front half glued to cloth. Most have heavily painted features, with rest of doll cloth, or some had composition or celluloid lower limbs. If they had hair or bonnets, these were generally stapled on.

There were some expensive Boudoir dolls and most were imported from France.

They have the more classic beauty, often with faces painted on stiffened, shaped cloth like buckram. Hair is better and the cloth fingers are individually sewn.

Boudoir/Bed Dolls: With excellent quality and finely painted features and excellent quality clothes: 28" – $125.00; 32" – $175.00.

Dolls with composition heads, stapled on wigs and composition limbs: 28" – $70.00; 32" – $90.00.

27" Buckram face mask with cotton body and limbs with gutta percha lower arms. Original. Marks: Patented June 2, 1925/No. 1540384/Chas. Bloom Inc. New York. 27" – $125.00.

27" Buchram molded face, painted features and real hair lashes. Cloth, stockinet and flannel combination body. Silk and velvet clothes. Tag: France. 27" – $125.00.

27" Boudoir doll with portrait style head that has a silk covered mask face with oil painted features. All original. Courtesy Bonnie Stewart. 27" – $125.00.

28" Bed/boudoir doll with composition head and shoulder. Composition lower limbs. Painted features with beauty mark and painted lower lashes. Also has set in hair lashes. Courtesy Bonnie Stewart. 28" – $70.00.

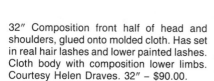

32" Composition front half of head and shoulders, glued onto molded cloth. Has set in real hair lashes and lower painted lashes. Cloth body with composition lower limbs. Courtesy Helen Draves. 32" – $90.00.

BRU

Bru dolls will be marked with the name Bru, Bru Jne, Bru Jne R, and some will have a circle dot (⊙), or a half circle and dot (⌒). Some will have paper labels on bodies-see below. Bru dolls are found on all kid bodies with bisque lower arms, on kid over wood, all wood or on all composition/wood jointed bodies. When there is a bisque shoulder plate, it too will be marked with Bru and a number over the edge of the shoulder. Prices are for beautifully dressed dolls with no damage any place and very clean.

BEBE BRU BTE SGDG

BEBE
BREVEE   SDGD
PARIS

CLOSED MOUTH DOLLS
Bru: All kid body, bisque lower arms. Closed mouth. 16" – $6,500.00; 18" – $7,400.00; 21" – $8,300.00.

Bru Jne: Kid over wood, wood legs, bisque lower arms: 12" – $5,800.00; 14" – $6,600.00; 16" – $8,500.00; 20" – $10,000.00; 25" – $14,500.00.
Bru Jne: All wood body: 16" – $7,800.00; 20" – $8,800.00.
Circle Dot or half circle: 16" – $7,400.00; 19" – $11,500.00; 23" – $14,500.00.
Brevete Bebe: 17" – $7,700.00; 20" – $9,000.00.

OPEN MOUTH DOLLS
Bru Jne R: Jointed composition body: 14" – $2,600.00; 17" – $3,600.00; 22" – $4,000.00; 25" – $4,600.00; 28" – $5,800.00.
Walker body, throws kisses: 18" – $3,800.00; 22" – $4,200.00.
Nursing Bru: Operates by turning key in back of head. Early, excellent quality: 12" – $3,400.00; 15" – $6,500.00; 18" – $7,200.00.

Not as good quality: 12" – $2,100.00; 15" – $3,700.00; 18" – $4,700.00.

High color, late S.F.B.J. type: 12" – $1,200.00; 15" – $2,200.00; 18" – $2,800.00.
Shoes: Marked Bru Jne shoes: 12"-17" size: – $65.00; 20" up sizes: – $100.00.

20" "Bebe Teteur" Nursing Bru. Composition jointed arms and rest kid over wood. Open mouth with key in back of neck. Marks: Bru Jne/8, on head. Bebe Bru/No.8, on shoulder plate. All original clothes with bottle marked: Bebe Teteur. 1879. Courtesy Jay Minter. 20" – $8,500.00 up.

36

Large Circle Dot Bru with all kid body, bisque lower arms. Closed mouth. Marks: ⊙ , on head. Courtesy Kimport Dolls. 23″ – $14,500.00.

16″ "Bebe Teteur" kid body with bisque lower arms, open mouth with key in back of head to operated nursing device. Marked on head and shoulder. Courtesy Jay Minter. 16″ – $4,300.00.

BYE-LO BABY

The Bye-lo baby was designed by Grace Storey Putnam and distributed by George Borgfeldt in 1922. Several German manufacturers produced the bisque heads including J.D. Kestner, Kling, and Alt, Beck &Gottschalck. The celluloid heads were made by Karl Standfuss of Germany and the all bisque Bye-lo's made by J.D. Kestner. Composition heads were made by the Cameo Doll Co. of New York. Bodies for the Bye-lo were made by K & K Toy Co. of New York and Schoenhut made an unauthorized Bye-lo in wood. The cloth bodies have curved "frog" legs, although there are some with straight legs, and the early dolls have celluloid hands. Later dolls as well as the composition head doll have composition hands. The doll's head will be marked with the date and designer and the cloth bodies are often stamped with the same information. The all bisque dolls will be marked with a number on the back and have a round paper label on front (often missing): Bye-lo Baby/Germany/Copr. by/G.S. Putnam. Prices are for clean, nicely dressed dolls with no damage.

All measured by head circumference except all bisque.
Bisque head: 10″ – $385.00; – 12″ – $485.00; 15″ – $775.00; 18″ – $1,300.00.

BYE-LO BABY
CARNIVAL DOLLS

Smiling mouth (very rare): 14″ – $4,400.00 up.

Socket head (bisque) on five-piece bent leg baby body: 14″ – $995.00; 17″ – $1,200.00.

Composition head: 10″ – $200.00; 12″ – $325.00; 15″ – $450.00.

Painted bisque head with cloth body, composition hands: 10″ – $250.00; 13″ – $365.00; 15″ – $550.00.

Wood by Schoenhut: Cloth body, wood hands: 13″ – $1,200.00.

Celluloid Bye-lo: all celluloid: 6″ – $145.00.

All bisque: Jointed only at hips and shoulders, painted eyes: 6″ – $375.00.

Jointed at neck, shoulders and hips. Glass eyes: 6″ – $600.00.

Cut pate with wig, glass eyes, jointed shoulders and hips: 6″ – $645.00.

Painted eyes, immobile, in different positions: 3½″ – $325.00.

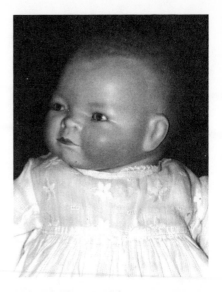

14½″ Bye-lo with "frog" cloth body and celluloid hands. Marks: 1923 By/Grace S. Putnam/Made in Germany. Courtesy Kathy Walters. 10″ head circumference – $385.00.

5″All bisque Bye-lo with paper seal on front. Painted hair and features. Jointed at shoulders and hips. Courtesy Turn of Century Antiques. 5″ – $375.00.

7″ All celluloid and jointed at shoulders only. Feathers and hat glued on. Marks: W, in circle/Japan. 1930's. 7″ – $36.50.

CARNIVAL DOLLS
CATTERFELDER PUPPENFABRIK

Painted cheek Carnival doll of early 1930's and referred to as "Chubby Kid". 25″ tall with a 19″ head circumference. Jointed only at shoulders. Painted features. Courtesy Jessie Smith (Canada). 19″ – $265.00.

15″ "Lone Ranger". All one-piece plaster carnival prize. Unmarked. Spray painted details. 15″ – $125.00.

CATTERFELDER PUPPENFABRIK

These dolls were made by Catterfelder Puppenfabrik at Catterfeld in Germany from 1902 until late 1920's. Some of the bisque heads may have been made by Kestner for them. The dolls will be marked: C.P. or with the full name Catterfelder Puppenfabrik, and some with a mold number also. Prices for clean, nicely dressed dolls with no damage.

Child doll: Composition jointed body. Open mouth. Mold #264, or marked C.P.: 17″ – $565.00; 23″ – $725.00.
Character Child: Composition jointed body. Boy or girl. Closed mouth and very character faces: Mold 215: 15″-16″ – $2,800.00; Mold 201: 15″-16″ – $2,500.00.
Babies: Wig or molded hair, five-piece bent limb baby body, glass or painted eyes: Mold 263: 15″ – $450.00; 20″ – $600.00; 25″ – $895.00.

Mold 201: 16″ – $1,400.00.

Mold 208: 14″ – $425.00; 18″ – $575.00.

23″ Marked C.P 264 child with open mouth and on fully jointed composition body. Marked: C.P. Courtesy Turn of Century Antiques. 23″ – $725.00.

CELLULOID DOLLS

Celluloid dolls were made in Germany, Japan, France, USA and Italy. They can date from the 1880's into the 1940's when they were made illegal as they can burn/explode if placed near an open flame/heat. Some are all celluloid, or can have celluloid heads on kid, cloth or ball jointed bodies. Some of the major German companies who used celluloid are: Kammer & Rheinhardt, Kestner, Kathe Kruse, Bruno Schmidt and Cuno & Otto Dressel. These companies often ordered the heads made by celluloid factories. Prices are for clean, nicely dressed dolls with no damage. Marks: Turtle in a diamond: Rheinische Gummi und Celluloid Fabrik Co. (Germany)

Large V with co, in circle and USA: Victoria Toy Co.

Minerva with helmet mark: Buschow & Beck (Germany)

SNF mark: Societe Nobel Francaise (France)

Eagle mark: Petitcolin (France)

3 M's mark: E. Maar & Sohn. (Germany)

Animal with spread wings and a fish tail, in square: Adelheid Nogler Innsbruck Doll Co. (Germany)

Jumeau mark: Unis. (France) 1950's.

All celluloid baby: Inset or painted eyes: 14" – $95.00; 16" – $125.00; 19" – $165.00; 22" – $195.00; 26" – $250.00.
All celluloid dolls-Germany: Jointed at neck, shoulders and hips: 5" – $18.00; 9" – $32.00; 12" – $60.00; 16" – $165.00; 18" – $200.00.

All celluloid-Germany: Jointed only at shoulders or at neck and shoulders only: 5" – $9.00; 7" – $18.00; 9" – $50.00.
Celluloid shoulder head: Germany, molded or wigged hair and PAINTED EYES; open or closed mouth, kid or kidaleen bodies, cloth bodies and can have any material for arms: 14" – $100.00; 17" – $145.00; 20" – $175.00.

Celluloid shoulder head: Germany, but with GLASS EYES: 14" – $150.00; 17" – $185.00; 20" – $225.00.

Celluloid socket heads: Germany. Glass eyes (allow more for flirty eyes), ball jointed bodies or five-piece bodies. Open or closed mouths: 15" – $195.00; 18" – $225.00; 22" – $300.00; 25" – $345.00.
Kathe Kruse: All original: 14" – $400.00; 17" – $650.00.
Kammer & Reinhardt (K star R): Mold 700 baby: 14" – $495.00.

Mold 701: 12" – $525.00.

Mold 714: 12" – $575.00.

Mold 715: 15" – $495.00.

Mold 717: 20" – $600.00; 25" – $950.00.

Mold 728: 15" – $495.00; 19" – $600.00.
All celluloid-Japan: 5" – $10.00; 8" – $20.00; 12" – $28.00; 16" – $85.00; 19" – $135.00; 22" – $165.00; 26" – $175.00.

14½" Celluloid head with oil cloth body, composition arms, painted blue eyes, closed mouth and all original clothes with leather pants. Marks: K star R 39/715. Made by Kammer and Reinhardt of Germany. Courtesy Kay Moran. 14½" – $495.00.

7″ Beautiful Siam baby made of all celluloid. Spray painted hair and finely detailed painted features. All original clothes. Courtesy Shirley Bertrand. 7″ – $85.00.

13″ Celluloid head with closed mouth and set eyes with lashes. On jointed body. Marks: Jumeau. Late 1940's. Courtesy Sylvia Bryant. 13″ – $100.00.

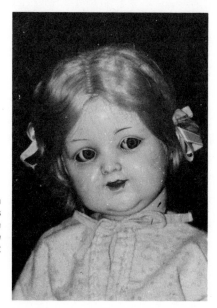

19″ Celluloid head on five-piece composition bent leg baby body, flirty sleep eyes with lids that drop over the eyes and open mouth with two upper teeth. Marks: K star R 728/7. Made by Kammer and Reinhardt. Courtesy Kimport Dolls. 19″ – $600.00.

CELLULOID DOLLS

12"All celluloid (painted) with molded hair, painted features and has one-piece body and head. Marks: Head of Indian. Made by Irokese Trading Co. operated by Louis Sametz, Westport, Conn. Ca. 1921. 12" – $95.00.

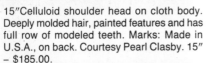

15"Celluloid shoulder head on cloth body. Deeply molded hair, painted features and has full row of modeled teeth. Marks: Made in U.S.A., on back. Courtesy Pearl Clasby. 15" – $185.00.

6"All celluloid jointed at the shoulders only. Molded on clothes and painted features. Marks: Made in Japan. Courtesy Kimport Dollls. 6" – $18.00.

Martha Jenks Chase of Pawtucket, Rhode Island, began making the Chase dolls in 1893, and they are still being made by members of her family. They all have oil painted features and are made of stockinet and cloth. They will be marked "Chase Stockinet" on the left leg or under the left arm. There is a paper label (often gone) on the backs with a drawn head:

The older Chase dolls are jointed at the shoulders, hips, knees and elbows, where the newer dolls are jointed at the shoulders and hips only with straight arms and legs. Prices for very clean dolls with only minor scuff.

Older Dolls: Babies: 16″ – $495.00; 20″ – $595.00; 24″ – $685.00.

Child: 12″ – $300.00; 16″ – $725.00; 20″ – $850.00.

Lady: 16″ – $1,150.00; 24″ – $1,800.00; Life size: $2,200.00.

Man: 16″ – $1,200.00; 24″ – $1,900.00; Life size: $2,400.00.

Black: 24″ – $2,200.00; 28″ – $2,800.00. **Newer Dolls:** Babies: 14″ – $165.00; 16″ – $195.00.

Child, boy or girl: 14″ – $165.00; 16″ – $195.00; 25″ – $300.00.
Portrait of George Washington: 22″-25″ – $2,800.00.

of women: 22″-25″ – $2,200.00-2,800.00.

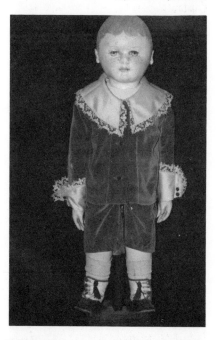

15″ Child with cloth body, oil painted features, molded painted hair and "jointed" (by sewn seam) elbows and knees. Courtesy Kimport Dolls. 15″ – $700.00.

27″ Chase boy with oil painted features and hair. "Jointed" at elbows and knees by sewn seam. Courtesy Helen Draves. 27″ – $1,600.00.

CHINA DOLLS

Almost all china dolls have black hair, but during the 1880's, blondes became more popular and by 1900, one out of three of the "common" type chinas were blonde. China dolls with brown hair (or eyes) are rarer than others. Prices for clean, nicely dressed dolls with no .cracks or repairs.

Adelina Patti: 1860's. Center part, roll curl from forehead to back on each side of head and "spit" curls at temples and above partly exposed ears: 14″ – $300.00; 18″ – $425.00.

Biedermeir or Bald head: Ca. 1840. Has bald head, some with top of head glazed black: Takes wigs: 14″ – $425.00; 20″ – $800.00. Early heads: 16″ – $1,000.00.

Bangs: Full across forehead. 1870's. Black hair: 16″ – $250.00; 20″ – $400.00; 26″ – $650.00. Blondes: 16″ – $285.00; 20″ – $450.00; 26″ – $700.00.

Brown Eyes: (Painted). Can be any hairstyle and date: 16″ – $500.00; 20″ – $900.00; 25″ – $1,200.00.

Common hairdo: Called "lowbrow" or "Butterfly". After 1905. Black or blondes. Wavy hairdo, center part with hair that comes down low on forehead: 8″ – $55.00; 12″ – $90.00; 16″ – $125.00; 19″ – $165.00; 23″ – $225.00; 27″ – $285.00.

Covered Wagon: 1840's to 1870's. Hair parted in the middle with flat hairstyle and has "Sausage" shaped curls around head: 16″ – $425.00; 20″ – $595.00.

Curly Top: 1845-1860's. Ringlet curls that are loose and over entire head: 16″ – $425.00; 20″ – $595.00.

Dolly Madison: 1870's-1880's. Loose curly hairdo with modeled ribbon and bow in center of the top of the head. Few curls on forehead. 14″ – $250.00; 18″ – $325.00; 21″ – $375.00.

Flat Top: 1850's-1870's. Black hair parted in middle, smooth on top with short curls around head: 17″ – $200.00; 20″ – $285.00; 24″ – $325.00.

Glass Eyes: Can have a variety of hairstyles. 1840's-1870's. 14″ – $1,200.00; 18″ – $2,100.00; 22″ – $2,600.00; 26″ – $3,000.00.

Japanese: 1910's-1920's. Can be marked or unmarked. Black and blonde hairdo. Can have "common" hairdo, or have much more adult faces and hairdo: 14″ – $100.00; 17″ – $145.00.

Man or Boy: Excellent quality, early date. Painted eyes: 14″ – $595.00; 16″ – $900.00; 20″ – $1,200.00 up.

Glass eyes: 14″ – $850.00; 17″ – $1,200.00; 20″ – $1,500.00.

Pet Names: 1905. Same as "common" with molded shirtwaist with name on front: Agnes, Bertha, Daisy, Dorothy, Edith, Esther, Ethel, Florence, Helen, Mabel, Marion, Pauline: 8″ – $115.00; 12″ – $155.00; 16″ – $195.00; 19″ – $245.00; 23″ – $295.00; 27″ – $350.00.

Pierced Ears: Can have a variety of hair styles. 14″ – $400.00; 18″ – $650.00. More must be allowed for rarity of hairdo.

Snood, Combs, any applied hair decoration: 14″ – $400.00; 17″ – $600.00.

15″ Glass eyes china. Curls in back half way up head and then comb marks. Ears partially exposed. Courtesy Kimport Dolls. 15″ – $1,200.00.

Spill Curls: With or without head band. Many individual curls across forehead and over shoulders with forehead curls continued to above ears. 14" – $300.00; 18" – $585.00; 22" – $650.00.

Wood body: Articulated with slim hips, china lower arms. 1850's. 12" – $850.00; Same with covered wagon hairdo: 12" – $500.00; 15" – $1,500.00.

16" Glass eye china with painted lashes (rare). Cloth body with leather arms. Courtesy Kimport Dolls. 16" – $2,000.00.

17" Man with side part hairdo and stipple around hairline. Cloth body with leather arms. Modeled on shirt front. Courtesy Kimport Dolls. 17" – $1,200.00.

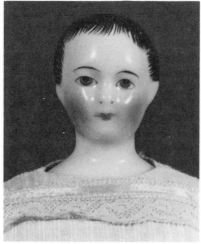

11" Rare early china with very "bald" style hairdo and heavy stippling around face and full across short hair style in back. All kid body with slim limbs. Courtesy Kimport Dolls. 11" – $1,200.00.

CHINA DOLLS

18″ Has fully exposed ears, curl pulled high off forehead and molded head band. (Author). 18″ – $995.00.

Close up of Ballerina face. Brush marks in brown hair, painted down cast eyes. 12″ – $450.00.

12″ Ballerina all china glazed with brown hair and beaded decoration, one-piece body, legs and head. Jointed at shoulders only. Delicate hands. Modeled on toes with painted-on slippers. (Author). 12″ – $450.00.

21″ Bald head china with cloth body and china limbs. Top of head is glazed black. Has detailed modeled ears. (Author). 21″ – $995.00.

13″ "Madame General" rare hairdo. Stippled around face with high rolled bun in back. Has light pink luster. Courtesy Kimport Dolls. 13″ – $895.00.

17½″ Brown eye Greiner style hairdo china. Cloth body with china limbs. Pink luster, exposed ears and has hair band molded near top of head in back. Back of hair is all small curls. Courtesy Kimport Dolls. 17½″ – $900.00 up.

15″ Very deep sloped shoulder head china with stippling around forehead like bangs. Courtesy Kimport Dolls. 15″ – $600.00.

CHINA DOLLS

14½" Little girl china with exposed ears, stripple painting around face and has small curls all over back of hairdo. Courtesy Kimport Dolls. 14½" – $350.00.

20" "Currier & Ives" hairdo china with spill curl, full bangs and molded band above curls. Cloth body and china limbs. Courtesy Kimport Dolls. 20" – $695.00.

24" "Spill Curl" hairdo with deep small curled bangs and roll curls vertically over top of head. Long curls over shoulders. Cloth body with china limbs. Courtesy Sylvia Bryant. 24" – $725.00.

19½" "Curly Top" china with cloth body and china limbs. Courtesy Kimport Dolls. 19½" – $595.00.

16" "Biedermier" style china with molded bosom and on kid body with china limbs. Three sew-holes front and back. Courtesy Kimport Dolls. 16" – $1,100.00.

17" Pink luster lady with upswept hairdo and curly bangs, called "Lady Baltimore". Probably made by Kling (Germany) and marked: 128-5. This doll head also came in tinted bisque. Courtesy Kimport Dolls. 17" – $995.00.

15" Japanese china with pierced ears into head. Courtesy Kimport Dolls. 15" – $145.00.

CLOTH DOLLS

Prices are for clean dolls with only minor scuffs or soil.

Alabama Indestructible Doll: All cloth with head molded and painted in oils, painted hair, shoes and stockings. Marked in torso or leg: Pat. Nov.9,1912 Ella Smith Doll Co. or Mrs. S.S.Smith/Manufacturer and dealer/The Alabama Indestructible Doll/Roanoke, Ala./Patented Sept. 26, 1905 (or 1907). 18" – $850.00.

Black: 18" – $1,400.00.

Arnold Print Works: "Brownie" dolls designed by Palmer Cox. Copyrighted in 1892. Printed on cloth and sold by the yard. Twelve dolls per yard: Canadian, Chinaman, Dude, German, Highlander, Indian, Irishman, John Bull, Policeman, Sailor, Soldier, and Uncle Sam: Yard-uncut: $250.00. Made-up: 8" – $90.00.

Art Fabric Mills: See printed cloth dolls.

Babyland: Made by E.I. Horsman from 1904 to 1920. Marked on torso, or bottom of foot. With oil painted features or printed features. With or without a wig. All cloth, jointed at shoulders and hips: 12" – $165.00; 18" – $425.00; 24" – $750.00; 30" – $900.00.

Black: 12" – $300.00; 18" – $550.00; 26" – $950.00.

Bruckner Cloth Dolls: Neck band label: Bruckner Doll/Made in U.S.A., or on shoulder: Pat'd July 8th 1901. Stiffened mask face with oil painted features. Cloth body and limbs. Child: 12" – $150.00; 16" – $225.00.

Black: 12" – $175.00; 16" – $250.00.

Two-headed doll. One Black and one White. (Topsy-Turvy): 12"-12½" – $325.00.

Charlie Chaplin: Made by Amberg & Sons and marked on bottom of foot: 17" – $300.00.

Chase, Martha Jenks: See that section.

Chad Valley: Label or paper tag: Chad Valley-Made in England. Cloth with velvet body, jointed neck, shoulders and hips. Painted or glass eyes, mohair wigs: Child with painted eyes: 12" – $125.00; 16" – $300.00; 18" – $395.00.

With glass eyes: 14" – $200.00; 16" – $400.00; 18" – $500.00.

Child representing Royal family (four in set-Princess Elizabeth, Princess Margaret Rose, Prince Edward, Princess Alexandria all have glass eyes). Prince Edward as Duke of Kent: 15" – $1,000.00. As Duke of Windsor: 15" – $1,000.00. Others: 15" – $800.00.

Columbian Doll: Marked before 1900: Columbian Doll/Emma E. Adams/Oswego Centre/N.Y. After 1905-1906: The Columbian Doll/Manufactured by/ Marietta Adams Ruttan/Oswego, N.Y. All cloth with hand painted features: 19" – $1,100.00.

Drayton, Grace: Dolly Dingle. 1923 by Averill Mfg. Co. Cloth with printed features: Marked on torso. 11" – $265.00; 14" – $300.00.

Chocolate Drop. 1923 by Averill Mfg. Co. Brown cloth with painted features and three tufts of yarn hair. 11" – $250.00; 14" – $350.00.

Hug Me Tight. By Colonial Toy Mfg. Co. in 1916. One-piece printed cloth: 11" – $150.00; 14" – $200.00.

Farnell's Alpha Toys: Marked with label on foot: Farnell's Alpha Toys-Made in England. Child: 14" – $195.00; 16" – $245.00. King George VI: 16" – $350.00. Palace Guard/Beefeater: 16" – $275.00.

Georgene Novelties: Marked with paper tag with both Georgene Averill and Madame Hendren. All cloth mask face and painted features. Yarn hair. Foreign costumes: 13" – $65.00; 18" – $85.00; 24" – $145.00. Children: 13" – $100.00; 17" – $165.00. Tear Drop Baby, has one tear drop painted on cheek: 16" – $265.00.

Kewpie Cuddles: Marked with cloth label sewn to seam: Made by Kreuger, Inc. Pat. #1785800. Fat, All cloth body, painted mask face, has tiny wings: 10" – $125.00; 13" – $195.00.

Lenci: See that section.

Liberty of London Royal Dolls: Marked with cloth or paper tag. Flesh colored cloth faces with stitched in and painted features. All cloth bodies. 1939 Royal portrait dolls are 8"-10" and included are Queen Elizabeth, Queen Mary, Queen Victoria and King George VI – $80.00. Other historical dolls: 10″ – $70.00.

Kamkins: By Louise Kampes. 1928 to 1934. Marked on back of head or foot, also has paper label, heart-shaped, on chest. All cloth with molded face mask and painted features, wigs and as boy or girl: 19″ – $800.00; 24″ – $1,400.00.

Kathe Kruse: Made in Germany from 1910. Modeled muslin heads, painted in oils and on jointed cloth bodies which are marked: Kathe Kruse, on sole of foot, and also may have the word Germany and a number. Later Kruse dolls will have a paper tag attached by a string also. Early cloth dolls: 15″-16″ – $1,000.00. Later dolls (1930's) with wigs: 15″-16″ – $550.00.

Madame Hendren: See Averill this section.

Mammy Style Black dolls: All cloth with painted or sewn features. Ca. 1910's: 14″ – $175.00; 17″ – $200.00. Ca. 1930's: 14″ – $100.00.

Mollye: Made from 1920 into 1950's. Designed and made by Mollye Goldman, International Dolls Co. Marked with paper tag. Babies. All cloth, painted face mask, mohair or yarn wigs: 17″-18″ – $85.00; 24″ – $100.00. Internationals. All cloth with face masks: 13″ – $65.00; 17″ – $85.00; 20″ – $100.00.

Philadelphia Baby: Also called "Sheppard Doll" as was made by J.B. Sheppard in late 1890's and early 1900's. Stockinet covered body with painted cloth arms and legs. Head is modeled and painted cloth: 21″-22″ – $1,200.00.

Printed Cloth Dolls: Advertising dolls to be cut out and stuffed such as: Rastus, The Cream of Wheat Chef: 18″ – $95.00. Aunt Jemima, set of four dolls: – $85.00 each. Dolls with printed on underwear: Cut-6″ – $65.00; 15″ – $145.00; 18″ – $160.00. Uncut-6″ – $75.00; 15″ – $155.00; 18″ – $170.00. Girls and boys with printed outer clothes: 6″ – $85.00; 15″ – $150.00; 18″ – $195.00. Uncut: 6″ – $95.00; 15″ – $165.00; 18″ – $225.00.

Rollinson Dolls: Molded cloth with painted features, head and limbs. Wigged or molded hair. Designed by Gertrude F. Rollinson and made by Utley Doll Co. Holyoke, Ma. Marks: stamp of doll in a diamond and around border: Rollinson Doll Holyoke, Ma. 17″-18″ – $900.00.

Smith, Mrs. S.S.: See Alabama in this section.

Steiff: Made in Germany early 1900's. All felt with jointed neck, shoulders and hips. Head seam runs straight down center of face. Can have glass or painted eyes. Painted hair or wigged. Metal button in ear and stamp on body: Steiff-trademark Made in Germany: 14″ – $650.00; 18″ – $850.00.

WPA Cloth dolls: Made 1935 into 1940's. Stockinette stuffed and stiffened head with cloth body with features painted in oils. Yarn hair glued on. Marks: location and number where made, such as #506, Elsworth, Kns. 18″ – $345.00; 22″-23″ – $425.00.

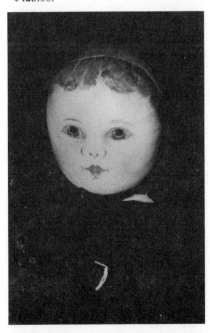

19″ "Columbian" Stamp: Columbian Doll/Emma E. Adams/Oswego Centre/N.T. Sold at the 1893 Columbian Exposition in Chicago. Courtesy Kimport Dolls. 19″ – $1,100.00.

CLOTH DOLLS

Walker, Izannah: Made in 1870's and 1880's. Modeled head with painted features in oils. Ears are applied. Cloth body and limbs. Hands and feet are stitched, or can have painted-on boots. Mark: Patented Nov. 4, 1873. Brushstroke hairdo. In fair condition: 16" – $2,800.00; In very good condition: 16" – $7,000.00. With two vertical curls painted in front of ears. In fair condition: 18" – $3,600.00; 24" – $4,200.00. In very good condition: 18" – $8,500.00; 24" – $12,000.00.

Wellings, Norah: See that section.

16" Photographic face doll. The real face is lithographed onto the cloth forming the face. May have been made by Dreamland Dolls, Horsman or Baron Henry Scotford. Doll is all cloth. Courtesy Kimport Dolls. 16" – $125.00.

12" "Topsy-Turvy" Colored and White headed doll. Mark: Albert Bruckner. Patented July 9, 1901. Courtesy Kimport Dolls. 12" – $185.00.

17" "Charlie Chaplin" All cloth with painted features and wool hair. Mark: Made by Louis Amberg & Son/Charlie Chaplin, on bottom of feet. Original, except bowler hat missing. Courtesy Earlene Johnston. 17" – $300.00.

17½″ All cloth girl with printed on clothes. Ca. 1890's. Courtesy Kimport Dolls. 17½″ – $195.00.

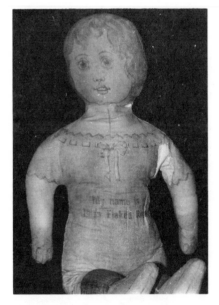

25″ All stamped cloth with "My name is Miss Flaked Rice" on torso. Printed on underclothes. 25″ – $285.00.

9″ "Mammy Doll" All one-piece black cloth with painted features. Sewn on clothes, earrings and head scarf. Made in New Orleans in 1941. 9″ – $45.00.

CRECHE FIGURES

Creche figures became very popular during the last part of the 1700's to the mid-1800's. Wealthy people commissioned well known artists and sculpturers to make figures for their scenes. The scenes did not just stop with the major, basic figures but included entire street scenes of people and animals, as well as items such as fruit for market scenes, and children, selling stalls, buckets, baskets, any number of items that fit into the scene.

The early Creche figures were gesso over wood head and limbs, a wire frame, fabric covered body. These figures have extremely fine detailed heads with carved hair

or in scale finely curled wigs. They have in-set glass eyes and the modeling of the features and limbs are truly a work of art. The later figures have a terra-cotta head and limbs and a wire formed body that is fabric covered. The eyes are painted with only a few having glass eyes, and detail workmanship is not as outstanding as early figures.
Older Creche: Early gesso over wood: Lady: 13″ – $395.00; 20″ – $795.00.

Man: 13″ – $595.00; 20″ – $895.00.

Child: 11″ – $295.00; 14″ – $400.00.
Later Creche: Terra-cotta: 13″ – $195.00; 16″ – $295.00.

22½″ Early Creche figure with gesso over wood, inset glass eyes, carved hair with applied decoration. Wire and cloth body and wood limbs. Late 1700's. Courtesy Kimport Dolls. 22½″ – $900.00.

14″ Woman and 15″ man Creche figures. Carved wood head and limbs with light layer of gesso. Inset glass eyes. Courtesy Kimport Dolls. 14″ – $425.00; 15″ – $645.00.

23½″ Terra-cotta Creche figure of an older lady. Has inset glass eyes and is all original. Courtesy Kimport Dolls. 23½″ – $525.00.

13″ Creche figure of gesso over carved wood. This one has a finely detailed, in scale wig. Inset glass eyes, wood limbs and cloth over wire armature body. Courtesy Kimport Dolls. 13″ – $395.00.

DEP

Many dolls, both French and German, bear the mark DEP. as part of the mold description, but the dolls referred to here are marked ONLY with the DEP. and a size number, are on a French body that sometimes bears the Jumeau sticker or stamp. Some of these DEP or marked heads will also have the red stamp: Tete Jumeau and/or the artist "check" marks. The early DEP. marked dolls will have a closed mouth and be of extremely fine quality in bisque and art work, and date from the 1880's. Dolls with this mark of the 1890's into 1900 will still have fine quality bisque and the later they become the higher the face color, and they will have painted lashes under the eyes only and most will have hair eyelashes over the eyes. The early dolls will have outlined upper lips and the later ones will not.

It is almost certain that a great many of the DEP. marked heads were acutally made in Germany by either Simon & Halbig, the most likely candidate, or by Kestner. Price for nicely dressed, clean dolls with no damage. Sample mark:

DEP
10

Open mouth DEP.: 14″ – $700.00; 18″ – $925.00; 25″ – $1,500.00; 30″ – $2,000.00.

Closed mouth DEP.: 14″ – $1,200.00; 18″ – $1,800.00; 25″ – $2,600.00; 30″ – $3,000.00.

28″ Marked: DEP./12 and has Jumeau sticker on body. Closed mouth. Head most likely made in Germany by Simon and Halbig for Jumeau. Note double chin. (Author). 28″ – $2,800.00.

28″ Marked: DEP./12, along with a "2" in black paint and "1" in red (both colors fired in). Closed mouth, painted lashes over and under eyes and body has Jumeau sticker: Bebe Jumeau/Diplome d Honneur. (Author). 28″ – $2,800.00.

25″ Marked: DEP./10. Excellent quality bisque with heavy, perfect feathered eyebrows and on Jumeau body. Open mouth. Courtesy Jay Minter. 25″ – $1,500.00.

13″ Marked: DEP. and has a Tete Jumeau stamped body. The body is five-piece mache with modeled-on boots and stockings with maroon band. Open mouth, deep set eyes with hair lashes and painted lashes under eyes. Courtesy Jay Minter. 13″ – $700.00.

20″ Marked: DEP./8, along with red stamp: Tete Jumeau. Sleep eyes with painted lower lashes, open mouth and has pierced ears. Courtesy Kay Moran. 20″ – $1,100.00.

DOLL HOUSE DOLLS

7″ Bride and Groom doll house dolls. She has a solid dome and he has a modeled-on mustache. Both have painted features, and original clothes. Courtesy Turn of Century Antiques. Doll house man or lady with molded hair/wig and painted eyes: 6″-7″ – $125.00-145.00. Man or women with glass eyes/wigs: 6″-7″ – $300.00-400.00. Grandparents or molded-on hats: 6″-7″ – $165.00-195.00.

DRESSEL, CUNO & OTTO

The Dressel firm was founded in 1700, but very little is known of them until 1863. They were located in Sonneberg, Thuringia, Germany and Cuno and Otto were the sons of the founder. The Dressel firm was listed as dollmakers by 1873 and they produced bisque head dolls with jointed kid, or cloth bodies as well as the ball-jointed composition/mache bodies. Some of their heads were made for them by Simon & Halbig. In 1906 they registered the trademark for "Jutta" and by 1911 they were also making celluloid dolls. Prices for clean, undamaged and nicely dressed dolls. Sample marks:

C.O.D

"Holz Masse"

Babies: Marked C.O.D., but without the word "Jutta": 14" – $300.00; 18" – $400.00; 24" – $600.00.
Child: On jointed composition body; open mouths: 15" – $265.00; 18" – $325.00; 22" – $400.00; 25" – $525.00.
Child: Open mouth and on kid, jointed body: 14" – $200.00; 18" – $300.00; 24" – $475.00.
Jutta: Baby, open mouth and five piece bent limb body: 14" – $435.00; 17" – $550.00; 20" – $695.00; 24" – $925.00; 26" – $1,200.00.

Toddler body: 14" – $535.00; 17" – $650.00; 20" – $795.00; 24" – $1,050.00; 26" – $1,300.00.

Child marked with or without the S&H. #1914, 1348, etc.: 17" – $425.00; 20" – $500.00; 24" – $600.00; 27" – $825.00; 30" – $1,250.00.
Lady Dolls: 1920's with adult face, closed mouth and on five-piece composition body with thin limbs and high heel feet. Mark: 1469: 14" – $1,100.00; 16" – $1,400.00.
Character Dolls: Closed mouths and painted intaglio eyes: 12" – $1,500.00; 14" – $2,300.00; 17" – $2,800.00.

Composition: Shoulder head of 1870's. Can have glass or painted eyes, molded hair or wig and on cloth body with composition limbs with molded-on boots. Will be marked with Holz-Masse:

With wig: 17"-18" – $375.00; 24" – $450.00.

Molded hair: 17"-18" – $350.00; 24"-26" – $425.00.

Right: 30" Marked Jutta 1349/S & H /14. Sleep eyes, open mouth with four teeth. Composition jointed body. Left: 30" Marked: Handwerck 109. and in carriage is a 14" "Dream Baby" twins marked: 341/A.M. Courtesy Glorya Woods. 30" Jutta – $1,500.00.

DRESSEL, CUNO & OTTO

12″ Bisque shoulder head on kid body with lower arms. Open mouth. Marks: Holz Masse/12/0. 12″ – $165.00.

20½″ Bisque shoulder head on kid body with bisque lower arms. Marks: C.O.D. 93-2 Dep. Courtesy Pat Timmons. 20½″ – $365.00.

23″ Marked: C.O.D. 52 Jutta 1914 12½. On five-piece bent limb baby body. Courtesy Yesterday's Child. 23″ – $595.00.

13½″ Baby with bisque head on five-piece bent limb baby body and marked: C.O.D. 4/0. Germany. Courtesy Yesterday's Child. 13½″ – $300.00.

E. Denamur of Paris made dolls from 1885 to 1898. After 1875 his business was known as "le Maison de Bambin". The E.D. marked dolls seem to be accepted as being made by Denamur, but they may have also been made by E. Dumont, Paris. Composition and wood jointed bodies. Prices for nicely dressed, clean and undamaged dolls.
E.D. marked child: Closed mouth: 14" – $2,100.00; 18" – $2,500.00; 22" – $2,800.00; 25" – $3,300.00; 29" – $3,900.00.
E.D. marked child: Open mouth: 16" – $1,400.00; 20" – $1,900.00; 25" – $2,300.00.

22" Closed mouth marked E. 8 D. Wood and composition jointed body, pierced ears. Courtesy Jay Minter. 22" – $2,800.00.

20" Marked: E. 8 D Depose. Open mouth with sculptured porcelain teeth. Composition jointed body. 20" – $1,900.00.

EINCO - Joseph Eisenmann & Co. made dolls in Furth, Bavaria. This doll ca. 1914. 13" Painted bisque socket head on five-piece bent limb baby body. Intaglio painted eyes and open/closed mouth. Marks: Einco/7½/-Germany. Courtesy Kimport Dolls. 13" – $400.00.

EDEN BEBE

Fleischmann & Bloedel of Paris, Furth & Bavaria. Founded in 1873 and joined S.F.B.J. in 1899. Marks: Eden Bebe/Paris. Eden Bebe with closed mouth and open mouths will be found on composition jointed bodies. Prices for nicely dressed, clean and undamaged dolls.

Eden Bebe: Open mouth: 15″ – $1,000.00; 18″ – $1,500.00; 22″ – $1,950.00.
Eden Bebe: Closed mouth: 15″ – $1,500.00; 18″ – $2,200.00; 22″ – $2,800.00.

23″ Marked: Eden Bebe/Paris. Has closed mouth and huge paperweight eyes, pierced ears and looks very much like an F.G marked doll. Courtesy Turn of Century Antiques. 23″ – $2,900.00.

21″ Marked: Eden Bebe Paris/9/Depose. Open mouth and on all papier mache body. 21″ – $1,950.00.

ELLIS, JOEL
FAMLEE

Made in 1873 and 1874 these dolls are also called "Springfield's" as Joel Ellis made the dolls under the name Co-operative Manufacturing Co. Springfield, Vt. All wood, with tenon and mortise joints and have metal hands and feet. Painted features and molded hair. Doll in overall good condition and does not need to be dressed. 12″ – $825.00; 15″ – $995.00; 18″ – $1,400.00.

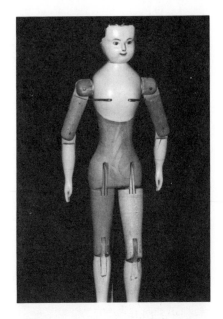

18″ Joel Ellis. All wood with mortise and tenon joints. Painted features and metal hands and feet. Made from two different woods where normally they were made of one kind of wood. Courtesy Kimport Dolls. 18″ – $1,400.00.

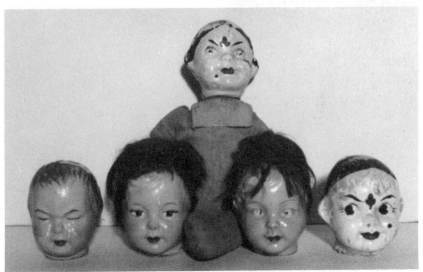

FAMLEE DOLL — Famlee dolls have composition heads with a metal threaded socket in the neck to screw onto the body. The body is cloth with composition lower arms. These dolls came in sets from three to twelve heads to a box with extra clothing. Made by Berwick Doll Co. and Change-O-Doll Co. N.Y. Mark: Pat. Apr.12, 21, on metal neck piece. Prices are for mint sets with no cracks or chips. 18″ three heads in box: $350.00; three heads, not in box: $165.00. Prices will be higher for more heads.

FASHION DOLLS, FRENCH

These "adult" style dolls were made by a number of French firms from about the 1860's on into 1930's. Many will be marked only with a number, or have a stamp or sticker on the body (some of these will be stamp or label from the store they were sold from and not the maker). Of all the ladies of fashion the most desirable are the Huret and Rohmer. Next in desirability is the fully articulated wood or blown kid body dolls. Some of these dolls will have bisque lower arms and/or legs, or metal limbs. The most available seems to be the F.G. marked Fashions. Prices are for dolls in perfect condition with no crack, chips nor repairs and in beautiful old or newer, appropriate clothes.

Articulated wood or blown kid bodies and limbs (some have bisque lower arms): 16" – $2,900.00; 20" – $3,500.00.

Articulated with bisque lower legs and fine feet detail: 16" – $3,600.00; 20" – $4,300.00.

Marked Huret or Rohmer: 16" – $4,200.00; 20" – $5,400.00.

Huret Portrait Lady: 18" – $9,800.00.

Marked Jumeau body/number on head: 14" – $1,900.00; 18" – $2,800.00; 24" – $3,700.00.

Marked F.G. All kid body: With swivel neck: 14" – $1,200.00; 17" – $1,500.00.

Marked F.G. All kid body. One-piece shoulder and head: 12" – $625.00; 15" – $900.00; 18" – $1,250.00.

Rare incised Huret portrait lady that has a fully articulated body with metal hands. Very adult face with painted eyes. Courtesy Barbara Earnshaw. 20" – $9,800.00.

Head marked F.G. and on Gesland cloth covered body that is jointed at shoulders, hips and knees. Bisque hands and lower legs. Swivel neck on shoulder plate. Courtesy Barbara Earnshaw. 17" – $3,200.00.

Marked F.G. Gesland cloth covered body with bisque hands and lower legs: 14" – $2,600.00; 17" – $3,200.00; 21" – $3,600.00.

Marked F.G. On Gesland cloth covered body with composition or papier mache hands and legs: 14" – $1,800.00; 17" – $2,400.00; 21" – $2,800.00.

Smiling "Mona Lisa". With kid body with leather arms and stitched fingers, or bisque lower arms. Marked with letter on head: 13" – $1,400.00; 17" – $2,700.00; 21" – $3,200.00.

Unmarked with numbers only: With one-piece head and shoulder: Extremely fine quality: 12" – $900.00; 16" – $1,400.00; 20" – $1,800.00.

Unmarked with numbers only: With swivel neck and extremely fine quality: 14" – $1,400.00; 18" – $1,800.00.

26" Jumeau fashion with blue stamp on body: Jumeau/unreadable/Paris. Applied ears, swivel neck on bisque shoulder plate. All kid body with leather arms. Portrait style head. Original wig. 26" – $3,900.00.

22" Jumeau fashion with swivel head on bisque shoulder plate and kid body with bisque lower arms. Portrait style head. Courtesy Turn of Century Antiques. 22" – $3,400.00.

FASHION DOLLS, FRENCH

12″ Smiling "Mona Lisa" Fashion with the letter R on head. Swivel neck on bisque shoulder plate and all kid body. Courtesy Jay Minter. 12″ – $1,200.00.

F. Gaultier (earlier was spelled Gauthier) is the accepted maker of the F.G. marked dolls. These dolls are often found on the cloth covered, or all composition marked Gesland bodies. The Gesland Freres firm was operated by two brothers with one of them having the initial F. The dolls will be marked F.G. along with a number, or the F.G. in a scroll: ⌐F.G.

For dolls marked: F + G see next section.

Child with closed mouth. Excellent quality bisque, no damage and dressed ready for a collection: 14″ – $2,300.00; 16″ – $2,600.00; 19″ – $2,900.00; 22″ – $3,200.00.

Child with closed mouth, but high face color, no damage and well dressed and ready to display: 14″ – $1,400.00; 16″ –
$1,600.00; 19″ – $2,000.00; 22″ – $2,400.00.

Child with open mouth. Excellent quality, no damage and dressed ready to display: 14″ – $1,000.00; 16″ – $1,200.00; 19″ – $1,600.00; 22″ – $1,800.00.

Child with open mouth. With high face color, very dark lips, no damage and dressed ready to display: 14″ – $500.00; 16″ – $650.00; 19″ – $850.00; 22″ – $1,000.00.

Marked F.G. Fashion: See "Fashion, French" section.

Child on marked Gesland body: Bisque head on stockinet over wire frame body with composition or bisque lower limbs. Closed mouth: 16″ – $2,500.00; 19″ – $3,400.00; 25″ – $4,400.00.

Marked F.G. on 22″ Gesland body. Open mouth: 15″ – $1,200.00; 18″ – $1,900.00.

21″ F.G in scroll bisque head with closed mouth, pierced ears and on boxwood tree all wood body with "pin" jointed knees, ankles and wrists. Ca. 1878-1880. 21″ – $3,600.00.

F.G. BEBE

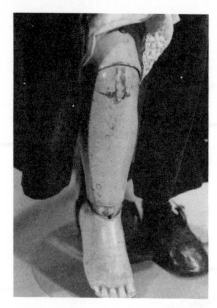

Shows the jointing of the ankles and knees on the all-wood body marked F.G. child.

26″ Marked F.G. in scroll with large paperweight eyes, closed mouth, pierced ears and feathered eyebrows. On composition jointed body. 26″ – $4,200.00.

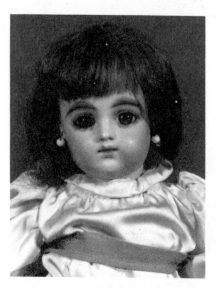

15½″ Marked with F.G in scroll on fully jointed composition body. Closed mouth, heavy feathered eyebrows and pierced ears. Courtesy Kimport Dolls. 15½″ – $2,300.00.

Dolls that are marked F + G were made in the 1960's in France and are reproductions from the originals. These dolls can be in bisque, have a china glaze and be "Fashions" or children. They are extremely well done reproductions and are not marked with the makers mark in any way. The kid bodies on the fashion-type will be dirty, have pin holes stuck into them, and/or have a place where a seal has been placed and removed so it looks like it originally had a label. These dolls apparently were meant to be frauds. They will have old glass eyes and are generally very well done and not easily seen as reproductions.

For information of F + G dolls, you are referred to an article in the Sun Flower Antique Doll Club Regional Souvenir Book, *U.F.D.C. Doll News*, Nov.1967, U.F.D.C. Boston Convention Book 1967, and to Virginia Chrostowsi's article in *Yesterday's Children*, Region 14 Souvenir Book of 1974. 17″ – $300.00.

17″ Marked: F + G on head. China glazed porcelain with old glass eyes, closed mouth and swivel head on bisque shoulder head. All kid body. Made in France in 1960's. 17″ – $300.00.

FLANDERS, HARRIET — 11″ All composition with painted features. Has molded yellow and glued on yarn hair. Marks: Harriet Flanders/1937. Courtesy Jay Minter. 11″ – $90.00.

26″ Flirty, unsleeping eyes operated by pull strings at base of head in back. Closed mouth with dark line between lips. On French jointed composition body. Marks: 103/16/X. Made by Fouquet and Douville in early 1890's. This firm obtained two French and one German patent for eye movement in 1891. 26″ – $3,600.00.

FROZEN CHARLOTTE

It is not known which came first, the ballad, or the doll, but in 1865, the ballad about "Young Charlotte" was most popular. The ballad is about a vain young lady who goes to the ball, with her friend Charles, in a very light cape as she does not want to muss up her gown. The night is cold and as the sled moves through the snow young Charlotte freezes and Charles dies of a broken heart. The entire ballad appears on page 107 of *Antique Collector's Dolls, Vol. I.*

Frozen Charlotte and Charlie figures can be all china, partly china, such as the hair or boots, stone and fine quality porcelain. They can have molded hair, painted bald heads, or take wigs. The majority have no joints with hands extended and legs separate but unjointed. They generally came without clothes, and they can have painted-on boots, shoes and socks, or be bare footed.

It must be noted that in 1976 a large amount of the 15½"-16" "Charlies" were reproduced in Germany and are excellent quality. It is almost impossible to tell these are reproductions.

Prices are for dolls/figures without any damage. More must be allowed for unusual hairdos or molded eyelids.

All china glazed with black or blonde hair and excellent quality of painting and unjointed: 1"-2" – $25.00; 4"-6" – $60.00; 8"-10" – $135.00; 12" – $200.00.

Bald head with wig, unjointed: 7" – $175.00; 10" – $235.00.

Charlie: Unjointed, molded hair, pink flesh tones to head: 13" – $265.00; 16" – $375.00; 18" – $525.00.

China or "Parian" (untinted bisque): Molded hair, jointed at shoulders. Not damaged and excellent quality: 4" – $110.00; 8" – $250.00; 11" – $365.00; 14" – $500.00.

Stone Bisque: Unjointed, molded hair. No damage and medium to excellent quality of painting: 4" – $30.00; 8" – $55.00.

Stone Bisque: Jointed shoulders, molded hair and not damaged: 4" – $45.00; 8" – $70.00.

Black Charlotte or Charlie: Unjointed and no damage: 3" – $50.00; 6" – $70.00; 8" – $90.00.

Jointed shoulders. No damage: 3" – $70.00; 6" – $90.00.

Molded on clothes or bonnet: Unjointed, no damage and medium to excellent quality: 6" – $95.00; 9" – $145.00.

Dressed in original clothes: Unjointed Charles or Charlotte. No damage with figure and clothes in excellent condition: 6" – $80.00; 8" – $150.00.

Jointed at shoulders. Original clothes. No damage and in excellent condition: 6" – $165.00; 8" – $260.00.

7" "Frozen Charlie" in original evening clothes that are glued on. Modeled, painted-on shoes. Courtesy Helen Draves. 7" – $100.00.

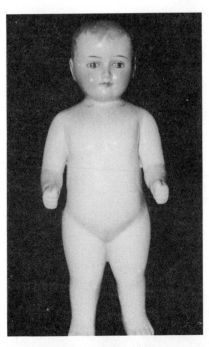

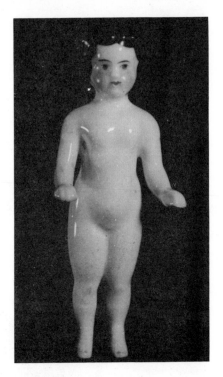

15½" "Frozen Charlie". All china glazed and tinted flesh tone. Blonde painted hair and painted features. Courtesy Helen Draves. 15½" – $375.00.

5" China glaze "Frozen Charlotte" Marks: 100, on back. 5" – $60.00.

FREUNDLICH, RALPH

Ralph Freundlich of the Freundlich Novelty Co. made dolls in New York and began operating in 1923. His dolls will be all composition or cloth and composition. Most will bear a cardboard tag and doll will be unmarked or will have the doll's name on the head, but no manufacturer name.
Baby Sandy: All composition with molded hair, sleep or painted eyes. Marked: Baby Sandy, on head. Original clothes, excellent condition composition with no chips, cracks or crazing: 8" – $125.00; 11" – $175.00; 14" – $225.00; 19" – $400.00.

With light crazing and nicely re-dressed: 8" – $85.00; 11" – $95.00; 14" – $100.00; 19" – $200.00.

Dummy Dan: See photo for description. Original and no chips, cracks or crazing: 21" – $275.00. Light Craze: $150.00.
General Douglas MacArthur: Portrait doll of all composition, painted features and molded hat. Jointed at shoulders and hips. Excellent condition and original: 18" – $185.00.

Clothes dirty and light craze: 18" – $95.00.
Military Dolls: All composition with painted features and molded hats. Can be man or woman. In excellent condition, original and no crazing: 15" – $135.00.

Light craze and clothes in fair condition: 15" – $85.00.

71

FREUNDLICH, RALPH

21″ Composition head, cloth hands, body and legs. Painted features. All original. Tag: The Ventriloquist Man/Dummy Dan/Ralph A. Freundlich. Courtesy Bonnie Stewart. 21″ – $275.00.

The Fulper Pottery Co. made doll heads from 1918 to 1921. The heads were developed for the Horsman Doll Co. and the heads were socket heads with composition jointed bodies or they were shoulder heads with jointed kid bodies. Since the Fulper dolls are all American-made with American materials, they are sought after by the collectors of Americana, even if the quality of the heads does not match those made in Germany and France. Sample marks:

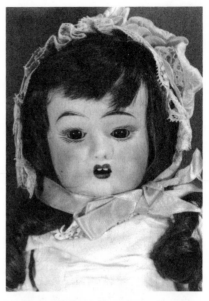

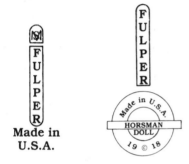

Made in U.S.A.

22" Marked Fulper with open mouth and two upper teeth. Bisque shoulder head on kid body with bisque lower arms. Fairly well painted and good quality bisque. Courtesy Jay Minter. 22" – $565.00.

Child: Fair to medium quality bisque head painting. Open mouth. No damage, dressed ready to place into collection:

Composition body: 14" – $365.00; 16" – $435.00; 21" – $525.00.

Kid body: 16" – $395.00; 21" – $495.00.
Child: Poor quality bisque (white chalky look, crooked mouth and poorly painted): Composition body: 16" – $200.00; 21" – $325.00.

Kid body: 16" – $185.00; 21" – $300.00.

Baby: Bent limb baby body. Fair to medium quality bisque. Open mouth. No damage, dressed well. Good artist work on features: 18" – $525.00; 25" – $825.00.
Toddler: Same as for baby, but on toddler straight leg body: 18" – $550.00; 25" – $850.00.
Baby: Poor quality bisque and painting: 18" – $200.00; 25" – $450.00.
Toddler: Poor quality bisque and painting: 18" – $250.00; 25" – $500.00.

G & S

Dolls marked with G & S, or G.S. were made by Gans and Sayfarth of Germany who operated from 1909 through the early 1930's. They also used their full name on dolls heads.
Child: Composition jointed body, open mouth. Good quality bisque and dressed and ready to display in a collection: 16" – $285.00; 20" – $350.00; 22" – $395.00; 26" – $450.00.
Baby: Bent limb composition baby body. Nicely dressed and in perfect condition: 18" – $495.00; 23" – $650.00.

G & S
GLADDIE

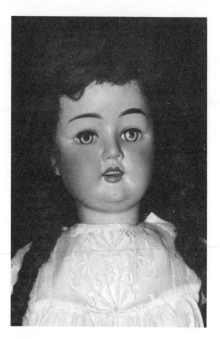

24" Bisque head on jointed composition body, sleep eyes and open mouth. Marked: G & S/Germany/6. Courtesy Kay Moran. 24" – $425.00.

20" Bisque head on composition jointed body. Large blue celluloid over tin sleep eyes, open mouth. Marks: Gans ✗ Sayfarth. Courtesy Margaret Gunnel. 20" # $350.00.

GLADDIE

"Gladdie" the "Laughing Child" was designed in 1927 and on the market in 1928-1929. The head can be made of ceramic material which is painted, or it can be fired-in bisque. The body is cloth and the limbs are composition. The doll head will be marked: Gladdie/copyright by/Helen W. Jensen. Modeled from a two-year old girl, the doll is mostly found dressed as a boy.

Gladdie: With painted ceramic head, in perfect condition with no rubs or paint chips and dressed ready to place in a collection: Molded hair, glass eyes and open/closed mouth: 17"-18" – $875.00.

Same as above but with fired-in color bisque head: 17"-18" – $2,450.00.

18" "Gladdie" with painted ceramic head, open/closed mouth, sleep eyes and molded hair. Marks: Gladdie/copyright by/Helen W. Jensen. 18" – $875.00.

The dolls marked with G.K. and four numbers with dot in middle (example: 32.24, 36.16, 41.28, etc.) could have been made by a number of German makers that include Kuhnlenz, Knoch or Krauss, or none of these. Until more information is forthcoming the maker remains unknown. The majority of these G.K. with four numbers (dot between two sets of numbers) can be extremely "French" looking and above average artist work, or of medium quality of workmanship.

Child style doll: Closed mouth, paperweight set eyes, feathered eyebrows, jointed composition body. Perfect bisque, well dressed and ready to display: 16" – $895.00; 20" – $1,100.00; 23" – $1,400.00.

Same as above but on kid body with swivel head on bisque shoulder plate: 16" – $795.00; 21" – $1,000.00.

Child: With open mouth, excellent bisque head, well dressed: 15" – $425.00; 19" – $550.00; 23" – $750.00.

Small size: Excellent bisque head, glass eyes, closed mouth, five-piece composition or mache body: 7½"-8" – $295.00.

Same, but with open mouth: 7"-8½" – $150.00.

15" Socket bisque head on bisque shoulder plate, kid body with bisque lower arms and stitched toes. Paperweight set eyes, closed mouth and pierced ears. Marks: G.K/34.32. Courtesy Kimport Dolls. 15" – $895.00.

GOEBEL

The Goebel factory has been in operation since 1879 and located in Oeslau, Thur, Germany. The interwoven W.G. mark has been used since 1879. William Goebel inherited the factory from his father, Franz Detley Goebel. About 1900, the factory only made dolls, doll's heads and porcelain figures. They worked in both bisque and china glazed items. The Goebel marks are:

WG

Child doll: Open mouth, composition jointed body, sleep or set eyes with head in perfect condition, dressed and ready for a collection: 16" – $295.00; 20" – $395.00; 24" – $495.00.

Character: Molded hair that can be in various styles, with or without molded flowers or ribbons, painted features and on five-piece papier mache body. No damage and dressed to go into a collection: 6" – $325.00; 8" – $400.00.

Character Baby: Open mouth, sleep eyes, on five-piece bent limb baby body, nicely dressed and not damaged: 14" – $365.00; 17" – $450.00; 21" – $550.00.

GOEBEL
GOOGLY

17" Bisque shoulder head with open mouth, set eyes and heavy painted eyebrows. Kid body. Marks: Crown/interwoven WG. Courtesy Kimport Dolls. 17" – $325.00.

GOOGLY

Bisque head with glass sleep or set eyes to side, closed smiling, impish or watermelon style mouth, original composition body. Molded hair or wigged. Not damaged in any way, nicely dressed:
Armand Marseille: #240: 11" – $1,600.00.

#253: 8" – $725.00; 12" – $950.00.

#258: 8" – $800.00; 12" – $1,300.00.

#310 "Just Me": 8" – $900.00; 12" – $1,200.00.

#310 Painted bisque: 8" – $385.00; 12" – $625.00.

#323: 8" – $625.00; 12" – $850.00.
Demalcol: 8" – $300.00; 11" – $425.00; 14" – $650.00.
Heubach Einco: 14" – $5,800.00.
Heubach (marked in square): 8" – $825.00; 12" – $1,350.00.
Heubach Kopplesdorf: #318: 9" – $1,200.00; 14" – $2,000.00.

#319: 12" – $1,000.00.

Kestner: #165: 12″ – $3,300.00; 16″ – $4,000.00.

#221: 12″ – $4,000.00; 16″ – $5,200.00; 18″ – $6,500.00.

Kammer * Rinehardt (K star R): #131: 12″ – $4,300.00; 15″ – $6,800.00.

P.M. (Otto Reinecke): #950: 8″ – $825.00; 12″ – $1,350.00.

S.F.B.J.: #245: 8″ – $1,000.00; 14″ – $5,000.00.

Steiner, Herm: 8″ – $625.00; 12″ – $850.00.

All bisque googlies: Jointed at hips and shoulders, painted on shoes and socks. Molded hair or wig, glass eyes, closed mouth. In perfect condition with no chips, cracks or hairlines. Nicely dressed: One piece body and head, swivel neck, glass eyes: 5″ – $625.00.

Swivel neck, painted eyes: 5″ – $395.00.

Jointed knees and elbows: 5″ – $1,600.00.

Composition face: Very round composition face mask, or all composition head with wig, glass eyes to side and closed impish watermelon style mouth. Body is stuffed felt. In original clothes and all in excellent condition with no crazing: 10″ – $525.00; 12″ – $725.00.

Fair condition, crazing and few cracks: 10″ – $200.00; 12″ – $350.00.

Painted eyes: Composition or papier mache body with painted-on shoes and socks. Bisque head with painted eyes to side, closed smile mouth and molded hair: Not damaged and nicely dressed: 8″ – $400.00; 12″ – $600.00.

Disc eyes: Bisque socket or shoulder head with molded hair (can have molded cap), closed mouth and inset celluloid discs in large googly eyes: 10″ – $895.00.

8″ Marked: SW & Co./405/16. All bisque googly with one-piece body and head, sleep eyes and closed mouth. Made for Strobel & Wilken Co., Cincinnati, Ohio, distributors. Doll made in Germany. Courtesy Turn of Century Antiques. 8″ # $875.00.

12″ A.M. 253. Five-piece composition body, bisque head with glass eyes and closed smile mouth. Courtesy Turn of Century Antiques. 12″ – $950.00.

GOOGLY

8"Heubach googly. Glass eyes and on five-piece papier mache body that is wire jointed at shoulders. Marks: Heubach, in square 3/0. Courtesy Kimport Dolls. 8" – $825.00.

11" Marks: Demalcol/5/0/Germany. Five-piece composition body and bisque head with set glass eyes, watermelon smile closed mouth. Courtesy Ruby Stuart. 11" – $425.00.

8" Marked: 323 A.M. googly on five-piece papier mache body. Painted-on shoes and socks. Closed smile mouth. Courtesy Jay Minter. 8" – $625.00.

The Greiner marked dolls were made by Ludwig Greiner of Philadelphia, PA, U.S.A. Thses dolls were made from 1858 into the 1880's. The heads are made of papier mache and they can be found on various bodies, such as all cloth, which are very often homemade, have leather arms, and some were on the Lacmann bodies that have stitched joints at the hips and knees and are very wide at the hip line. These bodies will be marked J. Lacmann's Patent March 24th 1874, in an oval. The Greiner heads will be marked: Greiner's Patent Doll Heads/Pat. Mar. 30, '58. Also: Greiner's/Improved/Patent heads/Pat. March 30,'58. And: Greiner's Patent Doll Heads/Pat. Mar.30'58. Ext. '72.

Greiner doll: Can have black or blond molded hair, blue or brown painted eyes, be on a nice homemade cloth body with cloth limbs, or a commercial cloth body with leather arms. Dressed for the period and clean with head in perfect condition with no paint chips and not repainted:

With '58 label: 18″ – $800.00; 22″ – $1,100.00; 25″ – $1,300.00; 28″ – $1,600.00; 31″ – $1,900.00; 35″ – $2,200.00; 38″ – $2,600.00.

With '72 label: 18″ – $400.00; 22″ – $600.00; 28″ – $800.00; 30″ – $950.00.

With either year label, head chips, or repainted, or small chips and not dressed well: 18″ – $200.00; 23″ – $250.00; 25″ – $350.00; 28″ – $400.00; 30″ – $485.00; 35″ – $525.00.

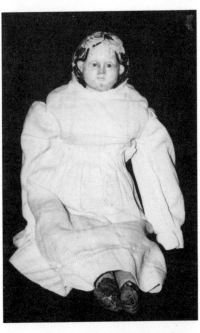

16″ Papier mache shoulder head with molded hair. On commercial cloth body with leather arms. Marks: Greiner's/Patent Doll Heads/Pat. Mar. 30, '58. Courtesy Kimport Dolls. 16″ – $650.00.

HALF DOLLS (PINCUSHION)

Half dolls can be of china, bisque, composition, papier mache or terra-cotta. Not all were used as pincushion dolls, but for such items as lamps, cosmetic or clothes brush, tea cozies, candy boxes, powder boxes and perfume bottle tops.

Most date from 1900 on into the 1930's with the majority being made in Germany, but many made in Japan. Generally they will only carry the mark of country and/or a number. The most desirable will be marked with the company, such as William Goebel: ⚇ W or Dressel, Kestner & Co.: ⌘ Company-marked half dolls often will have the marks on the underside of the figure. (Inside).

The most desirable half dolls will have both arms molded entirely away from the body so the hands are not touching the figure at all, jointed shoulders, bald head with wigs, with animals and those of children or men.

HALF DOLLS (PINCUSHION)

Arms/hands completely away from figure: China or bisque: 5″ – $125.00 up; 8″ – $195.00 up; 12″ – $700.00 up.

Arms extended, but hands attached to figure:

China or bisque: 3″ – $55.00; 5″ – $62.50; 8″ – $80.00.

Papier mache or composition: 4½″ – $20.00; 6½″ – $50.00.

Common figures with arms and hands attached to figure:

China: 3″ – $22.50; 5″ – $32.50; 8″ – $45.00.

Papier mache or composition: 3″ – $12.00; 5″ – $20.00.

Jointed shoulders: China, bisque: 5″ – $75.00; 8″ – $90.00; 12″ – $125.00 up.

Papier mache: 4″ – $27.50; 7″ – $65.00.

Wax over papier mache: 4″ – $37.50; 7″ – $85.00.

Children or men: 3″ – $35.00; 5″ – $55.00; 7″ – $85.00.

Jointed shoulders: 3″ – $55.00; 5″ – $80.00; 7″ – $125.00 up.

Lady with animal: Any material: 5″ – $75.00; 8″ – $145.00.

Japan marked: 3″ – $15.00; 5″ – $27.50; 7″ – $40.00.

3″ Half doll with arms modeled away from body, but hands are attached. Made in Germany. Courtesy Turn of Century Antiques. 3″ – $55.00.

12″ Bisque Half Doll with bald head, original wig, fired-in color mask and beauty mark. Both arms and hands molded away from body and hold fan. Mark: ⌒⌒. (Author). 12″ – $700.00 up.

3″ Half doll with both arms and hands molded to figure. Unmarked. 3″ – $22.50.

30″ Open mouth, bisque head on jointed composition/wood body. Head marked: 109 15/Dep/Germany/Handwerck/Halbig/6. Body is marked: Heinrich Handwerck/Germany/6, in red stamp. Head made for Handwerck by Simon & Halbig. Courtesy Jessie Smith. 30″ – $900.00 up.

26″ Open mouth, sleep eyes and marked: Handwerck 109. On jointed composition body. Courtesy Jay Minter. 26″ – $585.00.

HANDWERCK, HEINRICH
HANDWERCK, MAX

Heinrich Handwerck began in business in 1876 and was located at Gotha, near Walterhausen, Germany. They made dolls and doll bodies. Many of their heads were made by Simon & Halbig and other companies.

As early as 1891, Heinrich Handwerck had registered an 8-point star as a trademark and had registered, in Germany, such dolls as "Bebe Cosmopolite" (1895), Bebe Re'Clame" (1898), and "Bebe Superior" (1913). The 1913 "Bebe Superior" was actually made by Kammer & Reinhardt as they bought the Handwerck factory at the death of Heinrich in 1902, but continued to use the Handwerck trademarks.

In 1897 Heinrich Handwerck patented (in Germany) a ball jointed body #100297, and some of the doll bodies are so marked.

Some mold numbers from this company are: 12x, 19, 23, 69, 79, 89, 99, 100, 109, 119, 124, 125, 139, 152, 189, 199, 1200, 1290. A large number of their dolls will be marked with the makers name and no mold number. Marks used by Heinrich Handwerck are:

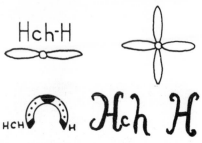

Child: Open mouth, sleep or set eyes, on ball jointed body. Bisque head with no cracks, chips, good wig, nicely dressed and ready to display: 16" – $300.00; 19" – $400.00; 23" – $475.00; 25" – $525.00; 27" – $650.00; 30" – $900.00; 33" – $1,200.00; 36" – $1,550.00; 39"-40" – $2,300.00.

HANDWERCK, MAX

Max Handwerck did not enter the doll field until 1900 and his factory was at Walterhausen,Thur,Germany. In 1901 he registered the trademark of "Bebe Elite", with these heads being made by William Goebel. In 1913 he registered "Cornouloid Doll" (Celluloid).

The Max Handwerck bodies were made following his 1913 American and German patents; they were hollow and constructed of paper/cloth. They were made by uniting two halves of thin material with staples at the overlapping edges. This inner body was covered by a slightly larger outer body that was united to the inner one by bonding. The outer body was kept together by flanges, which were trimmed and painted.

As for the marks on his dolls, the full name "Max Handwerck" generally was used, but some will have initials: M.H.
Child: Bisque head in perfect condition, sleep or set eyes, open mouth and on clean, good jointed composition body. dressed and ready to display: 16" – $300.00; 20" – $400.00; 24" – $475.00; 28" – $700.00; 32" – $1,100.00; 36" – $1,400.00; 40"-42" – $2,200.00 up.

Bebe Elite: Bisque head with no cracks or chips, sleep or set eyes, open mouth, flange neck on cloth body with composition limbs: 17" – $425.00; 21" – $575.00.

Socket head on jointed composition body: 17" – $435.00; 21" – $585.00.

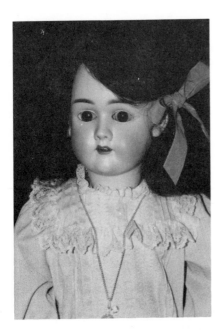

29″ Bisque head on fully jointed composition body. Sleep eyes and open mouth. Marks: Max Handwerck/Germany/4½. Courtesy Pearl Clasby. 29″ # $800.00.

22″ Bisque head with open mouth, sleep eyes with real hair lashes, and on fully jointed composition body. Marks: M.H./6½. Courtesy Kimport Dolls. 22″ – $425.00.

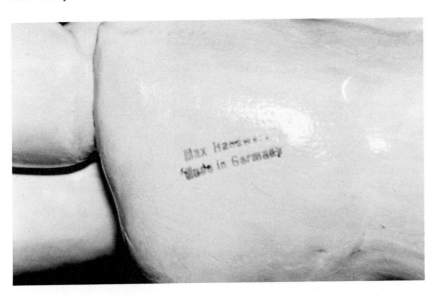

Mark on Max Handwerck patented body.

HEUBACH, GEBRUDER

The Heubach Brothers (Gebruder) factory was located at Lichte,Thur,Germany. The factory ran from 1863 into the 1930's. It is not known at what date they began making dolls, but they were known for fine porcelain bisque pieces, and it is known they began to produce character dolls in 1909 or 1910.

The Gebruder Heubach factory produced some very character dolls and babies with every imaginable expression that reflects almost every mood. They are generally small dolls. The Heubach dolls are often found on rather crude, poor quality bodies, but the character of the heads make up for the bodies. Marks:

Some Gebruder Heubach mold numbers: 28, 30, 37, 43, 45, 56, 58, 60, 63, 66, 68N, 69, 70, 71, 73, 74, 76, 77, 77G, 78, 79, 81, 83, 86, 87, 90, 91, 93, 94, 95, 101, 119, 122, 165, 750, 892, 0716, 0746, 1063, 1602, 3774, 4660, 5636, 5730, 5777, 6662, 6692, 6736, 6773, 6789, 6836, 6894, 6896, 6970, 7043, 7054, 7066, 7072, 7118, 7143, 7246, 7345, 7602, 7604, 7616, 7622, 7644, 7650, 7711, 7788, 7802, 7850, 7856, 7877, 7977, 8004, 8191, 8192, 8193, 8232, 8306, 8412, 8578, 8774, 9355, 9558, 9573, 10542, 10633, 96643.

Character dolls: Bisque heads, open/closed or closed mouths, intaglio painted eyes, on kid, papier mache, or jointed composition bodies. Molded hair or wigs: ALLOW MORE FOR GLASS EYES. No damage to head, nicely dressed and ready to add to a collection:

#5636: Laughing child. Intaglio eyes, jointed body: 12″ – $1,000.00.

Glass eyes: 12″ – $1,200.00.

#5777 & #9355: "Dolly Dimples". Ball jointed body: 16″ – $1,200.00; 22″ – $2,200.00.

#5730 "Santa": Incised "Santa". 20″ – $2,400.00.

#6736: Laughing child, wide open/closed mouth, molded lower teeth: 10″-12″ – $750.00; 16″-17″ – $1,500.00.

#6896: Pouty, jointed composition body: 19″ – $795.00.

#6969, #6970, #7246, #7407, #8017: Pouty boy or girl. (Allow more for glass eyes). Composition jointed body: 12″ – $1,500.00; 16″ – $1,800.00; 20″ – $2,500.00.

#7604: Laughing child. Jointed body, intaglio eyes: 12″ – $395.00.

#7616: Open/closed mouth with molded tongue. Socket or shoulder head. Glass eyes: 12″ – $1,000.00; 15″ – $1,350.00.

#7622: Molded hair boy, intaglio eyes, closed mouth and light cheek dimples: 12″ – $650.00; 16″ – $1,100.00.

#7644: Laughing child. Socket or shoulder head. Intaglio eyes: 14″ – $525.00.

#7711: Open mouth child, jointed body: 12″ – $435.00; 16″ – $850.00.

#7788: "Coquette" tilted head, molded hair, can have modeled ribbon in hairdo: 12″ – $700.00.

#7977 or #7877: "Stuart Baby". Modeled bisque bonnet: 12″ – $1,000.00; 14″ – $1,300.00; 16″ – $1,550.00.

Glass eyes: 12″ – $1,500.00; 14″ – $1,500.00; 16″ – $1,900.00.

#8191: Smiling openly, jointed body: 12″ – $725.00; 14″ – $850.00.

#8192: Open mouth: On five-piece body: 9″ – $300.00.

On jointed body: 14″ – $525.00; 17″ – $650.00.

#8774: "Whistling Jim". Eyes to side and mouth modeled as if whistling: 12″ – $800.00; 16″ – $1,100.00.

#10586 or #10633: Child with open mouth. Jointed body: 16″ – $400.00; 20″ – $600.00; 25″ – $825.00.

#10532: Open mouth. Jointed body: 12″ – $435.00.

Child with "dolly" type face: (non-character): open mouth, glass sleep or set eyes, jointed composition body, bisque head with no damage and dressed nicely and ready to place into a collection: 16" – $425.00; 19" – $595.00; 24" – $750.00.
Googly: Marked with a Heubach mark. Glass eyes: 8" – $825.00; 12" – $1,350.00.
#119: Braids coiled around ears of molded hairdo, intaglio eyes: 16" – $1,800.00.
Indian portrait of man or woman: 13" – $2,600.00.
Babies or infants: Bisque head, wigs or molded hair, sleep or intaglio eyes, open/closed "pouty" type mouths and on bent limb bodies: 8" – $295.00; 10" – $350.00.
#7926: Adult lady with adult body: 16" – $2,600.00.

12" Marked: 3394/Germany. Bisque head with painted eyes and closed mouth. Spray painted hair. Five-piece bent baby body. Courtesy Bonnie Stewart. 12" – $425.00.

12" Closed mouth, glass eyed doll on composition toddler body. Marks: Heubach, in square. Courtesy Jay Minter. 12" – $1,000.00.

16" Pouty Heubach with closed mouth and glass eyes. Jointed composition body. Marks: Heubach, in square. Courtesy Kimport Dolls. 16" – $1,800.00.

HEUBACH, GEBRUDER

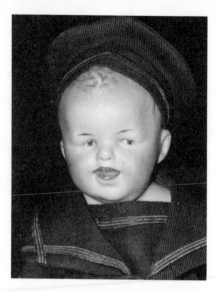

13″ Bisque head on jointed composition body. Lightly molded hair, intaglio eyes and closed mouth. Marks: Heubach, in square/3/Germany. Courtesy Kimport Dolls. 13″ – $1,300.00.

15″ Socket head with open/closed mouth and four painted upper teeth and two lower teeth. Jointed composition body. Marks: 3/Heubach, in square. Courtesy Helen Draves. 15″ – $1,200.00.

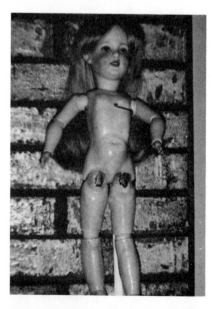

12″ Open mouth, glass eyes, and on jointed composition body. Marks: 8192/Germany/-Gebruder Heubach, Sunburst mark/G314. Courtesy Jay Minter. 12″ – $450.00.

20″ "Dolly Dimples". Sleep eyes with hair lashes, open smile mouth, cheek dimples. Marks: Dep./Dolly Dimple/H/Germany/8. On jointed composition body. Courtesy Rose Mills. 20″ – $2,000.00.

HEUBACH KOPPELSDORF

This company began in 1887 in Kopplesdorf, Germany. Marks from the Ernst Heubach of Kopplesdorf firm will be: E.H., the full name: Heubach Kopplesdorf or:

Some mold numbers of Heubach Kopplesdorf: 27X, 87, 99, 230, 235, 236, 237, 238, 242, 250, 251, 262, 271, 273, 275, 277, 283, 300, 302, 312, 317, 320, 321, 338, 340, 342, 349, 367, 399, 407, 410, 438, 444, 450, 452, 458, 616, 1310, 1900, 1901, 1906, 1909, 2504, 2671, 2757, 3027, 3412, 3423, 3427, 7118, 32144.

Child: On kid body with bisque lower arms, bisque shoulder head, open mouth. No damage and nicely dressed. 14″ – $185.00; 20″ – $295.00; 24″ – $395.00; 30″ – $750.00.

Child: Composition jointed body, open mouth, sleep or set eyes. No damage and nicely dressed: 10″ – $145.00; 14″ – $245.00; 20″ – $345.00; 24″ – $425.00; 30″ – $800.00.

Babies: On five-piece bent limb baby body, open mouth with some having a wobbly tongue and pierced nostrils. Sleep eyes. No damage and nicely dressed. 9″ – $200.00; 12″ – $325.00; 16″ – $425.00; 20″ – $525.00; 26″ – $750.00.

Back - 18″, left - 16″ and right - 15″ All marked: Heubach Kopplesdorf/300. Open mouths with 18″ one having four upper teeth and others two teeth. All have dimples, but only 18″ one has wobbly tongue. The 18″ & 16″ are on bent limb baby bodies and the 15″ on a toddler body. Courtesy Glorya Woods. 15″-16″ – $425.00; 18″ – $500.00.

HEUBACH KOPPELSDORF

Babies on toddler bodies: Same as above but with toddler body: 14″ – $525.00; 16″ – $585.00; 20″ – $650.00; 26″ – $850.00.
Infant: Molded or painted hair, sleep eyes, closed mouth, flange neck bisque head on cloth body with composition or celluloid hands. No damage and nicely dressed:

Mold #338: 12″ – $395.00; 14″ – $525.00.

#399 (White only): 12″ – $285.00.

#340: 12″ – $425.00; 15″ – $625.00.

#349: 12″ – $395.00.

Infant: Same as above but with fired-in tan or brown color: 12″ – $395.00; 14″ – $485.00.

Mold #452: Tan/brown bisque head and same color toddler body, open mouth and sleep or set eyes. Molded, painted hair. Earrings. No damage and originally dressed or re-dressed nicely: 12″ – $395.00.
Black or Dark Brown mold #320, #339, #399: Painted bisque head, on painted black or dark brown five-piece straight leg baby, or toddler cut body. Sleep eyes, molded, painted hair or wig. No damage and very minimum amount of paint pulls (chips) on back of head with none on face: 10″ – $350.00; 12″ – $400.00; 16″ – $600.00; 20″ – $800.00.
Character child: Molded hair, painted eyes and open/closed mouth. No damage and nicely dressed: 12″ – $400.00; 16″ – $695.00.

10″ Open mouth, pierced nostrils, sleep eyes with hair lashes. Toddler body and marked: Heubach Kopplesdorf/320-2/Germany. Courtesy Jay Minter. 10″ – $385.00.

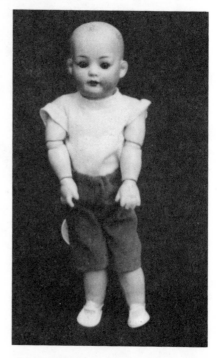

13½″ Bisque socket head on jointed body. Glass eyes and open mouth. Marks: Heubach Kopplesdorf/330/8/0 Germany. Courtesy Yesterday's Child. 13½″ – $395.00.

INDIAN DOLLS. Left to right: 13½" Plains doll totemic type in buckskin. Yellow and green beaded yoke. Buckskin dress is decorated with seed beads. Ca. 1890-1910. Center: 19" Plains doll with fully beaded yoke in yellow, green and blue. Stub arms, no hand contour. Cotton body. Buckskin dress hand sewn with sinew. Beaded facial features sewn into hide. Buffalo hair (rare) found growing from the softer side of the buffalo. Ca. 1900. Right: 10½" Nez Perce or Northern Plains doll with hide dress, red and blue stroud cloth yoke with blue beads and leggings. Small head with painted face and traces of human hair. Ca. 1880. All courtesy Margaret Mandel. Left – $350.00; Center – $600.00; Right – $250.00.

12¾" Plains fully beaded yoke on doeskin. All doeskin body stuffed with unprocessed wool. Handmade with cotton thread and sinew. Most of the fine beadwork is lazy stitched. Human hair strand still attached to scalp. Buckskin face partially painted red. Seed bead eyes and mouth. Ear bob of porcupine quill. Seed-bead choker is reminiscent of old time styles made of bugle beads or dentalia. White cotton petticoat (breechclothes, petticoats and porcupine quills occur only on the early dolls). Ca. 1860-1880. Courtesy Margaret Mandel. $400.00.

INDIAN DOLLS

Left: Crow with carved and painted wood head, body, legs and jointed arms. Human hair in three pig tails tied with trade cloth. Breast plate of seed beads. Indian tanned leather moccasins. Black felt sewn on leggins, green cloth shirt. 9½". Ca. 1900. Right: 13" Hopi male doll in dance costume. Kilt is hand woven cotton and lace belt is handmade. Unprocessed cotton stuffed brown cotton body. Embroidered features, yarn hair stitched on. Sead beads and tin form decorations. Ca. 1920. Courtesy Margaret Mandel. Left – $250.00; Right – $200.00.

8½" Miniature Apache cradle board. Fully beaded on doeskin covered frame. Green and white seed beads and white lined rose beads accenting geometric pattern. Ca. 1885. Courtesy Margaret Mandel. $350.00.

Cradle board 23" Woodlands (Great Lakes Region). Indian tanned hide, bow of cradle decorated with seed beads, pink ground, using maple leaf design. Dangles of larger pony beads and abolone shells (trade item). Example of Indians using a European doll (common china) and wrapping in trade cloth to make an Indian item. Courtesy Margaret Mandel. $300.00 up.

13″ Carved wooden head and hands in cradle board. Cotton stuffed body, commercially tanned hide, hand painted cradle, commercially printed wraps. Found with original note: "Indian carved by Lalooska, Hubbard, Oregon An Indian boy 18 years old. American name Don Smith". (Note: Don Lalooska is one of the foremost living Northwest Coast carvers today and his family cherishes his early work. Ca. 1930-1940. Courtesy Margaret Mandel. $350.00 up.

16″ Eskimo Indian. Indian tanned leather face, sewn on nose, embroidered eyes with feathered brows, sealskin mouth dyed red, loop pigtails of human auburn hair, wolf, seal and caribou clothes in style of 1st part of 20th century. 7½″ Carrying-baby with same features. Courtesy Margaret Mandel. $300.00 up

JULLIEN

Jullien marked dolls were made in Paris, France, from 1875 to 1904. The heads will be marked: Jullien and a size number. In 1892 Jullien advertised L'Universal and the label can be found on some of his doll bodies.

Child Doll: Closed mouth, paperweight eyes, French jointed composition/papier mache/wood body. No damage to bisque head and body in excellent condition. Well dressed and ready to display: 18″ – $2,900.00; 20″ – $3,100.00; 24″ – $3,400.00; 28″ – $3,800.00.

Child Doll: Same as above but with open mouth: 18″ – $1,500.00; 20″ – $1,900.00; 24″ – $2,200.00; 28″ – $2,600.00.

JULLIEN
JUMEAU

28" Marked Jullien on head. Open mouth, dimple in chin and heavy feathered eyebrows. 28" – $3,800.00.

French jointed body with bisque head marked: Jullien. Note French knees lack detail and are flush with lower leg. German bodies have rolls, dimples and detail at the knee area.

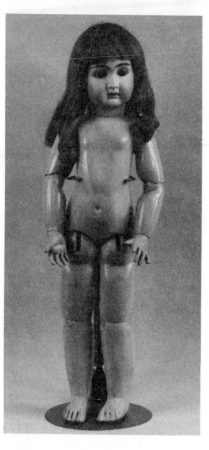

Paper label of 1892 on the body of the marked Jullien doll.

JUMEAU

Tete Jumeau: Marked with red stamp on head and oval sticker on body: Bebe Jumeau. Closed mouth, paperweight eyes, composition body with full joints or jointed but with straight wrists. Pierced ears with extra large sizes having applied ears. No damage at all to bisque head, undamaged French body, dressed and ready to place into a collection: 10" – $2,000.00; 12" – $2,000.00; 14" – $2,200.00; 16" –

$2,500.00; 19" – $2,900.00; 21" – $3,200.00; 23" – $3,400.00; 25" – $3,600.00; 28" – $4,400.00; 30" – $4,800.00.

Tete Jumeau: Same as above but with open mouth: 10" – $995.00; 14" – $1,400.00; 16" – $1,600.00; 19" – $1,900.00; 21" – $2,100.00; 23" – $2,300.00; 25" – $2,500.00; 28" – $2,800.00; 30" – $3,000.00.

1907 Jumeau: Incised 1907 and sometimes has "Tete Jumeau" stamp. Sleep or set eyes, open mouth, jointed composition body. No damage and ready to display: 14" – $1,100.00; 17" – $1,500.00; 20" – $1,800.00; 25" – $2,300.00; 28" – $2,800.00; 32" – $3,200.00.

E.J. Child: Head incised Depose/E.J. Paperweight eyes, closed mouth, jointed composition body with unjointed (straight) wrists. Larger size dolls will have applied ears. No damage on head or body, excellent quality clothes: 10" – $3,800.00; 14" – $4,600.00; 16" – $4,900.00; 19" – $5,200.00; 21" – $6,000.00.

Depose-Jumeau (incised): Head will be incised Jumeau/Depose and doll should have sticker on body: Bebe Jumeau. Closed mouth, paperweight eyes and on jointed composition body with straight wrists mostly. No damage at all and nicely dressed ready to display. 15" – $3,100.00; 18" – $3,900.00; 22" – $4,500.00; 25" – $5,200.00.

Long Face: Closed mouth, applied ears, paperweight eyes and on jointed composition body with straight wrists. Head generally marked with size number only and body will have label Jumeau sticker: No damage to head and body, and nicely dressed ready to display: 20"-21" – $10,000.00 up; 29"-30" – $12,000.00 up.

Portrait Jumeau: Closed mouth, usually large almond-shaped paperweight eyes and jointed composition body with straight wrists. Head marked with size number only and body with Jumeau stamp or label: 12" – $4,000.00; 16" – $4,800.00; 20" – $5,400.00.

Phonograph in Jumeau body: Bisque head with open mouth. No damage, working and nicely dressed ready to display: 20" – $2,800.00; 25" – $3,200.00.

Wire Eye (flirty) Jumeau: Lever in back of head operates eyes. Open mouth, jointed composition body with straight wrists: 20" – $5,200.00; 24" – $5,600.00.

Celluloid head: Incised Jumeau: 14" – $495.00.

Mold number 200 series character children: Marked Jumeau. No damage to bisque head or composition body: 19" – $10,000.00 up.

S.F.B.J. or Unis marked along with Jumeau: Open mouths. No damge to head or composition jointed body: 16" – $900.00; 20" – $1,150.00.

Closed mouth: 16" – $1,200.00; 20" – $1,600.00.

Two faced Jumeau: Has two different faces, one crying and one smiling, heads turn with knob on top usually covered with lacy hood. Open/closed mouths, jointed composition body. No damage and nicely dressed: 14" – $7,800.00.

Fashion: (Also see "Fashion" section): Bisque shoulder head on bisque shoulder plate (jointed neck), all kid and leather body, or will have bisque lower limbs. Head generally marked with size number and kid body may have a Jumeau stamp. No damage and dressed as lady and ready to display: 14" – $1,900.00; 18" – $2,800.00; 21" – $3,100.00; 26" – $3,900.00.

Composition body Lady: Marked Tete Jumeau on head. No damage and beautifully dressed: 18" – $4,800.00.

Mold 221: These small dolls (10") will also have a paper label: Jumeau. Adult style bisque head on five-piece body and painted-on shoes. Closed mouth and set glass eyes. Dressed in original ornate long gowns. No damage to head or body: 10" – $495.00.

Mold 306: Jumeau made after formation of Unis and mark will be: Unis/France in oval with 71 on one side and 149 on other, followed by 306/Jumeau/1938/Paris. Called "Princess Elizabeth". Closed mouth, paperweight or flirty eyes, jointed composition body. No damage and dressed ready to go into a collection: 20" – $1,300.00.

JUMEAU

29″ "Long Face Jumeau". Marks: 14, on head and on marked Jumeau body. Jointed body with straight wrists. Closed mouth and paperweight eyes. Original dress. Courtesy Jay Minter. 29″ – $12,000.00 up.

26″ Closed mouth Jumeau marked head and body. Courtesy Jay Minter. 26″ – $2,600.00.

26″ Incised E.J. Marked body and applied ears. Very pale excellent bisque with expressive features. Courtesy Turn of Century Antiques. 26″ – $7,000.00.

13″ Closed mouth marked Tete Jumeau on head and Bebe Jumeau on body. Courtesy Jay Minter. 13″ – $1,400.00.

22" Open mouth Jumeau marked 1907 on head and marked Jumeau body. This one also has the Tete Jumeau red stamp on head. Courtesy Jay Minter. 22" – $1,995.00.

14" Open mouth Jumeau marked on head and body. Courtesy Jay Minter. 14" – $1,400.00.

22" Jumeau Fashion with all kid body and bisque lower shoulder plate. (See Fashion section). Courtesy Turn of Century Antiques. 22" – $3,200.00.

KAMMER & REINHARDT

Kammer & Reinhardt dolls often have the Simon & Halbig name or initials along with their own mark, as a great number of heads were made for them. They were located in Walterhausen,Thur,Germany and began in 1895 although their first models were not on the market until 1896. The trademark of this company was registered in 1895. Marks:

S & H
126

Character Boy or Girl: Mold #101: Closed mouth, painted eyes, on jointed composition body or five-piece body. No damage, clean and nicely dressed: 8"-9" – $1,000.00; 14" – $1,800.00; 17" – $3,000.00.

Mold #101: GLASS EYES. Closed mouth and on fully jointed body. No damage and dressed: 16" – $3,800.00; 21" – $4,300.00.

Mold #102: Very rare character child. No damage head or body: 12" – $8,300.00; 14" – $8,800.00.

Mold #103 or #104: Extremely rare. No damage to head or body: 17" – $14,000.00.

Mold #107: Pursed closed mouth, intaglio eyes. No damage head or body: 15" – $5,800.00; 21" – $6,300.00.

Mold #109: Closed mouth, intaglio eyes and on fully jointed body. No damage and nicely dressed: 14" – $5,000.00; 19" – $6,800.00.

Mold #109: GLASS EYES: 20" – $12,000.00; 25" – $18,000.00.

Mold #112, #112x, #112a: Closed mouth, intaglio eyes, jointed body. No damage and nicely dressed: 14" – $4,800.00; 19" – $5,600.00; 22" – $6,000.00.

Mold #112, #112x, #112a: GLASS EYES: 16" – $7,800.00; 22" – $9,000.00.

Mold #114: Intaglio eyes, painted eyes, closed mouth and on five-piece or fully jointed body. No damage and nicely dressed: 8" – $1,200.00; 14" – $2,600.00; 18" – $3,900.00.

Mold #114: GLASS EYES: 18" – $6,000.00; 23" – $6,500.00.

Mold #117A, #117: Glass eyes, closed mouth, on fully jointed body or small sizes on five-piece body. No damage to head or body and nicely dressed: 9" – $1,500.00; 16" – $3,200.00; 18" – $3,800.00; 24" – $4,800.00; 28" – $5,500.00.

Mold #117, #117x: OPEN MOUTH. 16" – $1,600.00; 20" – $2,100.00; 24" – $2,800.00; 28" – $3,300.00.

Mold #117n: Open mouth and flirty eyes. Fully jointed body. No damge to head or eye mechanism, good body and nicely dressed: 16" – $800.00; 20" – $1,400.00; 26" – $2,000.00; 32" – $2,800.00.

Character Babies: Open/closed, closed mouths on five-piece bent limb baby body. Solid dome with painted hair or wigs. No damage to head and body in excellent condition. Nicely dressed and ready to display:

Mold #100: Called "Kaiser Baby". Intaglio eyes, open/closed mouth: 10" – $475.00; 16" – $650.00; 18" – $900.00.

Mold #100: GLASS EYES. Wig: 16" – $1,600.00; 18" – $1,900.00.

Mold #100: Black or tan: 10" – $900.00; 16" – $1,200.00.

Mold #115, #115a: 15" – $2,500.00; 18" – $3,200.00; 22" – $4,000.00. Toddler body: 15" – $3,200.00; 18" – $3,800.00; 22" – $4,600.00.

Mold #116, #116a: 15" – $2,000.00; 18" – $2,300.00; 22" – $2,900.00. Toddler body: 15" – $2,400.00; 18" – $2,800.00; 22" – $3,300.00.

Mold #116, #116a: OPEN MOUTH: 15" – $1,000.00; 18" – $1,600.00.

Mold #123, #124, #127: Add more for flirty eyes. 12" – $695.00; 16" – $850.00; 20" – $1,000.00. Toddler: 16" – $925.00; 20" – $1,200.00.

Character Babies: Open mouth, sleep eyes, on five-piece bent limb baby body. Wigs, may have tremble tongue or "mama" cryer box in body. No damage to head or body. Nicely dressed. Allow more for flirty eyes.

Mold #121, #122, #128: 14″ – $600.00; 18″ – $850.00; 22″ – $995.00. Toddler: 14″ – $850.00; 18″ – $1,100.00; 22″ – $1,500.00.

Mold #126: 12″ – $425.00; 15″ – $500.00; 20″ – $650.00; 25″ – $850.00. Toddler: 8″ – $375.00; 15″ – $575.00; 20″ – $850.00; 25″ – $1,250.00.

Mold #118A: 16″ – $1,600.00; 20″ – $2,000.00.

Child Dolls: Open mouth, sleep or set eyes and on fully jointed composition body. No damage to head or body and nicely dressed. Most often found mold numbers are 400, 403, 109, etc. Add more for flirty eyes:

16″ – $450.00; 18″ – $525.00; 22″ – $625.00; 26″ – $785.00; 30″ – $950.00; 33″ – $1,400.00; 36″ – $1,800.00; 38″ – $2,000.00; 42″ – $2,500.00.

Small Child Dolls: Open mouth, sleep or set eyes and on five-piece body. No damage and nicely dressed: 5″ – $200.00; 8″-9″ – $295.00.

Googly: Mold #131. Glass eyes, closed smile mouth and on five-piece body or fully jointed body. No damage and nicely dressed: 12″ – $4,300.00; 15″ – $6,800.00; 17″ – $7,200.00.

Celluloid: Babies will have kid, kidaleen or cloth bodies. Child doll will have fully jointed composition bodies. Open mouths. Some mold numbers: 225, 255, 321, 406, 717, 826, 828, etc.

Babies: 15″ – $400.00; 20″ – $575.00.

Child: 16″ – $450.00; 20″ – $625.00.

8″ "Peter and Marie" Marked K star R 101. Both are all original. Closed pouty mouths and painted eyes. Courtesy Jane Alton. 8″ – $2,800.00 each.

23″ Marked: K star R 117A. Closed mouth and set eyes. On fully jointed composition body. 23″ – $4,700.00.

KAMMER & REINHARDT

16" Marked K star R/Simon & Halbig/116a. Open/closed mouth and on a toddler body. Sleep eyes. Courtesy Jay Minter. 16" – $2,400.00.

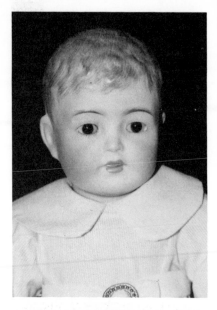

16" Socket head on fully jointed composition body, lightly molded brush stroke hair, sleep eyes and open/closed mouth. Marked: K star R/Simon & Halbig 127. Courtesy Helen Draves. 16" – $850.00.

29" Marked K star R/ S & H. Sleep eyes, feathered brows and open mouth. On fully jointed composition body. Courtesy Barbara Earnshaw. 29" – $950.00.

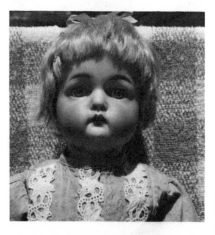

17" Marked: K star R/Halbig/1290 or 290. The top of the "1" is slightly visable above the hole in back of neck that secures the sleep eyes in shipment. On fully jointed compositon body. Courtesy Jane Walker. 17" – $525.00.

9½″ Bisque head on papier mache five-piece body with painted-on shoes and socks. Sleep eyes and open mouth. Marked S&H/K star R. Courtesy Kay Moran. 9½″ – $295.00.

24½″ Marked: Simon & Halbig/K star R/Germany 61. Papier mache and composition fully jointed body, open mouth and sleep eyes with hair lashes. Courtesy Kay Moran. 24½″ – $750.00.

21″ Marked: K star R/S&H/126. Has compositon head, open mouth and flirty eyes. Five-piece bent limb baby body. Courtesy Yesterday's Child. 21″ – $675.00.

16″ Marked: K star R/S&H/121. Five-piece bent limb baby body, sleep eyes and open mouth. Courtesy Yesterday's Child. 16″ – $695.00.

KESTNER, J.D.

The Johannes Daniel Kestner firm was founded in 1802 and his name was carried through the 1920's. The Kestner Company was one of the few that made entire dolls, heads and bodies. It was in 1895 that Kestner starting using the trademark of the crown and streamers found on some bodies. Most Kestner dolls are marked with both a letter and a number and some of these also will have a mold number and/or the initials J.D.K. (Samples: G-11,M-16,D-8). Sample marks:

B Made in 6
Germany
J.D.K.
126

F Germany K

Some Kestner mold numbers: 117, 127, 128, 128x, 129, 135, 137, 139, 140, 142, 143, 144, 146, 147, 148, 150, 151, 152, 153, 154, 155, 156, 157, 158, 160, 161, 162, 163, 164, 165, 166, 167, 168, 169, 170, 171, 172, 173, 174, 176, 178, 180, 182, 183, 184, 185, 186, 187, 188, 189, 190, 193, 194, 195, 196, 200, 211, 212, 213, 214, 215, 216, 217, 219, 220, 221, 226, 230, 234, 235, 237, 238, 241, 243, 245, 249, 252, 255, 257, 259, 260, 261, 262, 263, 264, 268, 270, 272, 280, 286, 319, 518, 639, 920, 1070, 1080, 1914.

Child Doll: Closed mouth, some appear to be pouties, sleep or set eyes, composition jointed body with straight wrists. No damage and nicely dressed to add to collection:

Mold #X: 14″ – $1,500.00; 17″ – $1,800.00; 20″ – $2,000.00; 24″ – $2,400.00.

Mold XI: 14″ – $1,600.00; 17″ – $1,900.00; 20″ – $2,100.00; 24″ – $2,600.00.

Mold #128x or 169: 14″ – $1,500.00; 17″ – $1,800.00; 20″ – $2,000.00; 24″ – $2,400.00; 28″ – $2,800.00.

Turned Shoulder Head: Closed mouth. Set or sleep eyes, on kid body with bisque lower arms. Both head and body undamaged and nicely dressed: 17″ – $950.00; 20″ – $1,100.00; 24″ – $1,500.00.

Turned Shoulder Head: Same as above but with open mouth: 17″ – $375.00; 20″ – $500.00; 24″ – $625.00.

Character Child: Closed mouth or open/closed mouth (unless noted). Glass or painted eyes, on jointed composition body. Plaster pate, good wig and no damage to head or body. Nicely dressed:

Mold #208: Painted eyes: 12″ – $1,600.00; 17″ – $2,900.00.

Mold #212: Glass eyes: 14″ – $2,000.00; 17″ – $3,200.00; 20″ – $3,600.00. Painted eyes: 14″ – $1,600.00; 17″ – $2,900.00.

Mold #224: 16″ – $525.00.

Mold #241: Open mouth, glass eyes: 16″ – $1,900.00; 20″ – $2,800.00.

Mold #249: 20″ – $1,000.00.

Mold #260: On toddler body: 16″ – $650.00; 20″ – $850.00.

Character Dolls: Boxed set with four heads and one body. 11″-12″. Usually has one head with open mouth and three with closed mouths and painted eyes. All heads in perfect condition, no damage to body and one outfit: Boxed set: $4,800.00.

Extra heads with painted eyes on old bodies and no damage to either. Mold numbers: 175, 176, 177, 178, 179, 180, 182, 184, 185, 186, 190, 208, 212, etc.: 11″-12″ – $1,600.00.

Same mold number in larger sizes. Painted eyes, closed or open/closed mouths: 16″ – $2,300.00; 18″ – $2,900.00.

Same mold numbers with GLASS EYES: 12″ – $2,000.00; 16″ – $2,800.00; 18″ – $3,400.00.

Child Doll: Open mouth, on fully jointed composition body, plaster pate (if original), sleep eyes, some set, not damaged in any way (head or body) and nicely dressed: Mold numbers: 129. 142, 144, 145, 146, 147, 152, 156, ,159, 160, 162, 164, 166, 167, 168, 174, 195, 196, 214, 215, etc. 14″ – $375.00; 17″ – $475.00; 20″ – $525.00; 26″ – $650.00; 30″ – $900.00; 36″ – $1,600.00; 42″ – $2,400.00.

Mold #143: 12″ – $525.00; 17″ – $725.00; 20″ – $850.00.

Mold #192: 14″ – $395.00; 17″ – $495.00; 20″ – $575.00.

Child Doll: Open mouth, sleep or set eyes, bisque shoulder head on kid body with bisque lower arms. No damage to head or body and nicely dressed. Includes mold numbers 147, 148, 149, 166, 195, etc. Add more for fur brow. 17″ – $425.00; 20″ – $500.00; 26″ – $625.00; 30″ – $850.00-950.00.

Mold #154 and #171: Most often found mold numbers. Open mouth and sleep or set eyes. No damage and nicely dressed. Jointed composition body: 15″ – $375.00; 18″ – $450.00; 22″ – $525.00; 27″ – $700.00; 32″ – $900.00; 40″ – $2,000.00.

Kid body with bisque lower arms: 15″ – $350.00; 18″ – $425.00; 22″ – $500.00; 27″ – $650.00; 32″ – $850.00; 40″ – $1,800.00.

Character Babies: On five-piece bent limb baby body, sleep or set eyes, open mouth and can be wigged, solid domed with painted hair, or lightly molded hair. Head and body not damaged and nicely dressed.

Mold #121, #142, #150, #151, #152: 12″ – $400.00; 16″ – $550.00; 20″ – $650.00; 25″ – $900.00.

Mold #211, #226, #260: 12″ – $400.00; 16″ – $525.00; 20″ – $725.00; 24″ – $1,100.00.

Mold #234, #235, #238: 16″ – $575.00; 20″ – $750.00; 24″ – $900.00.

Mold #237, #245, #1070 (HILDA): 12″ – $1,700.00; 16″ – $2,700.00; 20″ – $3,200.00. Toddler: 16″ – $3,300.00; 20″ – $3,700.00; 23″ – $4,200.00.

Mold #239: 12″ – $450.00; 16″ – $575.00.

Mold #247: 16″ – $625.00; 18″ – $1,200.00; 21″ – $1,600.00; 25″ – $1,900.00.

11″ Marked: 185, on head. Open/closed mouth, painted eyes and on jointed composition body. Courtesy Jane Walker. 11″ – $1,600.00.

KESTNER, J.D.

Mold #257: 14″ – $450.00; 18″ – $625.00; 21″ – $750.00; 25″ – $850.00.

Adult: Mold #162: Sleep eyes, open mouth, adult jointed composition body (thin waist and molded breasts) with slender limbs. No damge to head or body and dressed nicely as lady: 16″ – $850.00; 18″-19″ – $950.00.

Mold #172 "Gibson Girl": Bisque shoulder head with closed mouth, kid body with bisque lower arms, glass eyes. Undamaged head and body. Dressed as lady and ready to display: 12″ – $1,200.00; 17″ – $2,400.00; 21″ – $3,200.00.

Oriental: Mold #243: Olive fired-in color to bisque, matching color five-piece bent limb baby body (or jointed toddler style body). Wig, sleep or set eyes. No damage to head nor body and dressed in Oriental style outfit: 14″ – $2,200.00; 18″ – $2,800.00.

Small Dolls: Open mouths, five-piece or jointed bodies, wigs, sleep or set eyes. Dressed ready to display and no damage to head or body: 7″ – $250.00; 9″ – $325.00.

Trunks with wardrobes: Bisque head small doll as described above: 7″ – $550.00; 9″ – $750.00.

11″ Molded hair, intaglio eyes and open/closed mouth. On fully jointed composition body. Marks: 177, on head (incised). Courtesy Jane Walker. 11″ – $1,600.00.

22″ Marked: X1. Jointed body with straight wrists. Closed mouth and sleep eyes. Courtesy Turn of Century Antiques. 22″ – $2,400.00.

19″ Closed mouth Kestner on jointed composition body. Has deep painted line between lips. Marks: H 9/ 6(or C). Courtesy Jay Minter. 19″ – $2,000.00.

16½″ Hilda with sleep eyes on Kestner five-piece toddler body. Open mouth with two upper teeth. Marks: F Made in 13/Germany/-237/J.D.K. jr./1914/Hilda, along with ges. gesch running up one side of mark and N 1070 along other side. 16½″ – $3,300.00.

16½″ Hilda on Kestner toddler body. Dress may be original

10″ Marked: J.D.K./260. Open mouth, five-piece body with painted-on white socks and black shoes. Sleep eyes. Original wig. Courtesy Jay Minter. 10″ – $325.00.

14″ Kestner mold #143 with open mouth, sleep eyes and heavy feathered eyebrows. On fully jointed composition body. Courtesy Jay Minter. 14″ – $600.00.

KESTNER, J.D.

24″ and 26″ Kestner mold #171. Both have open mouth, sleep eyes with larger one having hair lashes. Both are on fully jointed composition bodies. Courtesy Turn of Century Antiques. 24″ – $575.00; 26″ – $650.00.

17″ Marked: G Made in 11/Germany/. Open mouth, sleep eyes and on jointed composition body. Original clothes. Small one is 12″ marked: A Made in 5/Germany. Open mouth, and on fully jointed composition body. Courtesy Betty Shelley. 12″ – $225.00; 17″ – $475.00.

20″ Marked: 149 Made in Germany C-7. Open mouth and on fully jointed composition body. 20″ – $525.00.

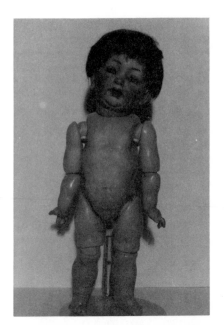

15" Marked: J.D.K. 211 and called "Sammy". Open/closed mouth and glass eyes. On toddler body. Courtesy Turn of Century Antiques. 15" – $495.00.

13" Marks: Made in Germany/152. Open mouth with two upper teeth and molded tongue. Set eyes and on five-piece bent limb baby body. Courtesy Jay Minter. 13" – $425.00.

22" Marked: J.D.K. 257/ 57/Germany. Flirty sleep eyes and open mouth. Five-piece bent limb baby body. Courtesy Yesterday's Child. 22" – $800.00.

16" J.D.K. 226 with sleep eyes and open mouth. On five-piece bent limb baby body. Courtesy Yesterday's Child. 16" – $525.00.

KEWPIE

All prices for dolls that have no chips, hairlines or breaks. (See Modern section for composition and vinyl Kewpies). Designed by Rose O'Neill and marketed from 1913.

Labels:

All bisque: One-piece body and head, jointed shoulders only. Blue wings, painted features with eyes to side. 1½" – $65.00; 2½" – $95.00; 4"-5" – $125.00; 6" – $150.00; 7" – $225.00; 9" – $350.00.
All bisque jointed at hips and shoulders: 4" – $400.00; 9" – $650.00.
Action Kewpie: Confederate Soldier. 3½" – $275.00; Farmer. 4" – $400.00. Gardner. 4" – $400.00. Governor. 3½" – $350.00. Groom with Bride. 4" – $400.00.

Guitar Player. 3½" – $300.00. Holding pen. 3" – $350.00. Huggers. 3½" – $300.00. On stomach. 4" – $350.00. Thinker. 6" – $385.00. Traveler. 3½" – $300.00. With broom. 4" – $350.00. With cat. 3½" – $350.00. With dog (Doodle). 3½" – $700.00. With helmet. 6" – $450.00. With outhouse. 2½" – $850.00. With rabbit. 2½" – $275.00. With rose. 2" – $275.00. With Teddy bear. 4" – $600.00. With turkey. 2" – $350.00. With umbrella and dog. 3½" – $750.00.

Button Hole Kewpie. $165.00.

Kewpie Doodledog. 3" – $600.00.

Hottentot. Black Kewpie. 3½" – $275.00; 5" – $350.00; 9" – $800.00.

Perfume Bottle. 3½" – $450.00.
Celluloid Kewpie: 2" – $28.00; 5" – $50.00; 9" – $120.00. Black. 5" – $125.00.
Cloth Body Kewpie: with bisque head, painted eyes: 12" – $1,500.00; with glass eyes: 12" – $2,900.00.
Glass Eye Kewpie: On chubby toddler, jointed body. Bisque head. Marks: Ges. gesch./O'Neill J.D.K. 12" – $3,800.00; 16" – $6,000.00.

13" Cloth body Kewpie with compostion head and lower arms. Tag on front of body. Courtesy Pearl Clasby. 13" – $325.00.

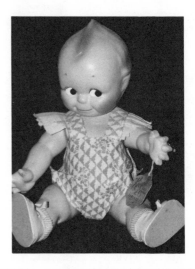

13" All composition Kewpie. Jointed at neck, shoulders and hips. Original clothes and tag. Penner collection. 13" – $175.00.

19″ "Kiddie Pal Baby" Cloth body with composition shoulder head and limbs. Disc jointed legs and arms are strung through shoulderplate. Molded, painted hair, open/closed mouth with two upper teeth with smile and dimples. Marks: Kiddie Pal Baby/Regal Doll Mfg. Co. Inc. Ca. 1926-1928. Courtesy Jeannie Mauldin. 19″ – $195.00.

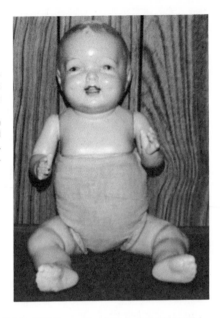

K & K. 17″ Bisque shoulder head on kid body with bisque lower arms, open mouth and set eyes. Marks: 38/K&K/45/Thuringia. Made for Kohle & Kohle of New York City in Germany. (Head). 17″ – $375.00.

17″ Marked: K&K 45 child on "mama" style cloth body with composition limbs. Head is bisque. Courtesy Yesterday's Child. 17″ – $375.00.

KLEY & HAHN

Kley & Hahn operated in Ohrdruf, Germany, from 1895 to 1929. They made many different baby dolls, as well as extremely fine character children. Some of their molds are: 50, 52, 56, 66, 75, 76, 129, 130, 132, 138, 140, 141, 142, 143, 149, 150, 154, 156, 157, 158, 159, 160, 162, 167, 176, 179, 199, 210, 220, 250, 266, 277, 282, 331, 520, 522, 525, 526, 531, 536, 546, 549, 552, 568, 585, 680. Sample marks:

K & H   ≥K ⋲ H ≤

Character Child: Boy or girl. Painted eyes, closed or open/closed mouth, on jointed composition body. Undamaged head and body and nicely dressed. Mold #520, 523, 525, 526, 531, 536, 546, 549, 552: 16" – $2,500.00; 20" – $4,000.00; 24" – $4,400.00.

Same mold numbers on toddler bodies: 16" – $2,700.00; 20" – $4,200.00; 24" – $4,600.00.

Same mold numbers on bent limb baby bodies: 14" – $1,300.00; 17" – $2,400.00; 21" – $3,800.00; 25" – $4,200.00.

Same mold numbers with GLASS EYES: 14" – $1,800.00; 16" – $2,700.00; 20" – $4,400.00; 24" – $4,800.00.

Character Babies: Molded hair or wig, glass sleep or set eyes, or painted eyes, can have open or closed mouth. On bent limb baby body. No damage to head or body and nicely dressed. Mold numbers: 130, 132, 142, 150, 158, 162, 167, 176, 199, 522, 525, 531, 585, 680: 12" – $350.00; 16" – $500.00; 20" – $650.00.

Same mold numbers on toddler bodies: 14" – $400.00; 16" – $550.00; 18" – $625.00; 20" – $750.00; 24" – $950.00.

Mold #568: 16" – $650.00; 18" – $825.00; 21" – $950.00.

Mold #162 with talker mechanism in head: 17" – $850.00; 23" – $1,150.00; 26" – $1,800.00.

Mold #162 with flirty eyes and clock works in head: 18" – $1,000.00; 25" – $2,200.00.

12" Marked K & H in banner along with mold number 536/2/0. Cheek dimples, intaglio painted eyes and open/closed mouth. Jointed composition body. Courtesy Jane Walker. 12" – $1,600.00.

23" Bisque head with sleep eyes and open mouth, on fully jointed composition body. Marks: 250/KH/Walkure/3½/Germany. Courtesy Jay Minter. 23" – $595.00.

Mold #154, #157 Child: Closed mouth: 16″ – $2,000.00; 19″ – $2,500.00.

Open mouth: 16″ – $650.00; 19″ – $950.00.
Child Dolls: Walkure and/or 250 mold

mark. Sleep or set eyes, open mouth and on jointed composition body. Head and body undamaged and nicely dressed. 16″ – $295.00; 20″ – $495.00; 24″ – $625.00; 28″ – $725.00; 32″ – $1,100.00.

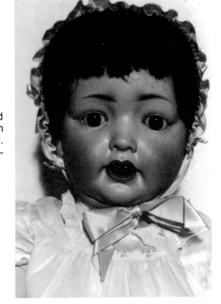

18″ Head circumference life size marked K&H baby. Has wobbly tongue in open mouth with upper teeth. On bent limb baby body. Courtesy Turn of Century Antiques. 24″ – $950.00.

12″ On bent limb baby body, open/closed mouth with two upper teeth. Glass sleep eyes. Marks: K & H/522. Courtesy Jay Minter. 12″ – $350.00.

KLEY & HAHN
KONIG & WERNICKE
KRAUSS, GEBRUDER

16″ Two-faced Kley & Hahn on bent limb baby body. Lightly molded hair and open/closed mouth. Courtesy Barbara Earnshaw. 16″ – $1,200.00.

16″ Two-faced baby with one side having glass eyes and other has painted eyes. Courtesy Barbara Earnshaw. 16″ – $1,200.00.

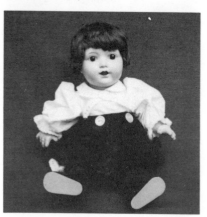

KONIG & WERNICKE. 16½″ Bisque head on five-piece bent leg baby body. Marks: K&W, in circle/298-9/Germany. Courtesy Yesterday's Child. 15″ – $450.00; 18″ – $545.00; 21″ – $625.00.

Toddler body: 15″ – $500.00; 18″ – $600.00; 21″ – $700.00.

Flirty eyes: 15″ – $525.00; 18″ – $625.00; 21″ – $725.00.

KRAUSS, GEBRUDER. 18″ Bisque head with molded brows, open mouth and on fully jointed composition body. Marks: 26/GBR 165 K/2/Germany. **Child:** 16″ – $350.00; 18″ – $425.00; 21″ – $500.00; 24″ – $595.00; 28″ – $625.00.

Baby: 14″ – $300.00; 17″ – $400.00; 22″ – $500.00.

Founded in 1910 by Kathe Kruse, the wife of a well known Berlin sculptor. Her first dolls were copies of a baby of the Renaissance period and of her own children. The heads were hand painted in oils. In 1916 she obtained a patent for a wire coil doll. These dolls were: Kathrinchen, a Dutch doll, Lutt Martin, Fritz, Christincen and Michel. In 1923 she registered, as a trademark, a double K with the first one reversed, along with the name Kathe Kruse.

After World War II Kathe Kruse dolls were made of plastics by the Rheinische Gummi Celluloid Fabrik Company of Germany. These plastics were first shown at the Toy Fair in Nuremberg in 1955. Marks: The early dolls had molded muslin heads that were hand painted, jointed cloth bodies and have Kathe Kruse, in script, along with a number and sometimes Germany, on the sole of the foot.

Early marked dolls: In excellent condition and with original clothes: 17″ – $1,100.00; 20″ – $1,500.00.

Excellent condition, but nicely redressed: 17″ – $650.00; 20″ – $800.00.

1920's dolls: With wigs, still have cloth bodies and oil painted heads: 17″ – $1,000.00; 20″ – $1,400.00.

Plastic dolls with glued on wigs, sleep eyes, or painted eyes. Markled with Turtle in diamond and number on head, on back are marked: Modell/Kathe/Kruse/and number: 16″ – $350.00.

16″ All plastic with glued on wig of human hair, sleep eyes with hair lashes, closed mouth. Marks: Turtle, in diamond/T 40, on head. Turtle mark/Modell/Kathe Kruse/T40, on back. 16″ – $350.00.

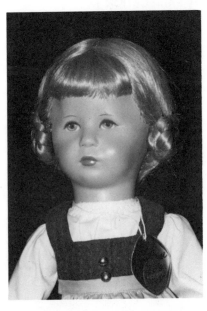

19″ "Riekchen" 1970. Cloth and rigid plastic, painted eyes. Tag: Kathe Kruse/Exclusive for Neiman-Marcus. Courtesy Jay Minter. 19″ – $400.00.

LANTERNIER

A. Lanternier & Cie (Company) of Limoges, France, made dolls from about the 1890's on into the 1930's. Prior to making doll heads, they made porcelain pieces as early as 1855. The doll's heads will be fully marked and will sometimes carry a name such as: Favorite, LaGeorgienne, Lorraine or Cherie. They are marked with an anchor, or Fabrication/Francoise, in a square, along with an A.L. or A.L.&Cie. The dolls are generally found on papier mache bodies, but can also be on composition jointed bodies. Marks:

LIMOGES
A L

FABRICATION
FRANCAISE

AL & Cie
LIMOGES

Child doll: Open mouth, set eyes, on jointed body. No damage to head nor body and dressed nicely. Good quality bisque with pretty face: 16″ – $625.00; 20″ – $725.00; 23″ – $850.00; 26″ – $1,000.00.

Poor quality bisque with very high coloring, or blotchy color bisque: 16″ – $400.00; 20″ – $475.00; 23″ – $525.00; 26″ – $645.00. **Character:** Open/closed mouth with teeth, smiling fat face, glass eyes, on jointed composition or papier mache body. Not damaged in any way and nicely dressed: Marked: TOTO: 16″ – $895.00; 18″ – $1,200.00; 22″ – $1,400.00.

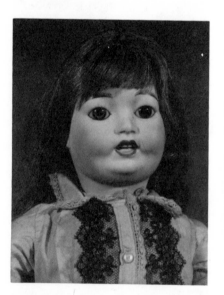

22½″ Bisque head with glass eyes and open/closed mouth and modeled teeth. Jointed papier mache body. Marks: Toto/A.L. & Cie/Limoges. Courtesy Kimport Dolls. 22½″ – $1,400.00.

14″ Open mouth with modeled teeth, large glass eyes with very long painted lashes. Marks: Frabrication/Francoise, in square/A.L.&Cie/Favorite. Courtesy Jay Minter. 14″ – $475.00.

22″ Marks:  Made by Louis-Aime Lejeune of St Marie-des-Fosses, France in 1915. Bisque head with closed smile mouth and detailed painted eyes. 22″ – $2,800.00.

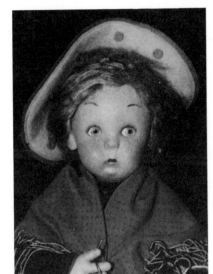

11″ Lenci. All felt with oil painted features. Clothes are felt and cloth. Made in 1930's. Courtesy Kimport Dolls. 11″ – $485.00.

25″ Lenci Boudoir doll with long thin limbs. All felt with oil painted features and organdy and felt clothes. Courtesy Kimport Dolls. 25″ – $1,300.00.

LENCI

Lenci dolls are all felt with a few having a cloth torso. They will be jointed at neck, shoulders and hips. The original clothes will be felt or organdy, or a combination of both. The features are oil painted and usually have eyes painted to the side. Sizes can range from 5″ to 45″. Marks: On cloth or paper tag: Lenci Torino Made in Italy. Lenci may be written on the bottom of the foot, or underneath one arm.

Children: No moth holes, very little dirt on clothes, doll as near mint as possible, doll in overall excellent condition: 14″ – $650.00 up; 16″ – $850.00 up; 18″ – $950.00 up; 20″ – $1,200.00 up.

Dirty, original clothes in bad condition or redressed: 14″ – $200.00; 16″ – $300.00; 18″ – $300.00; 20″ – $400.00.
Tiny Dolls: In excellent condition: 5″ – $125.00; 9″-10″ – $225.00.

Dirty, redressed or original clothes in bad condition: 5″ – $50.00; 9″-10″ – $85.00.
Ladies with adult faces: "Flapper" or "Boudoir" style with long limbs. In excellent condition: 24″ – $1,000.00 up; 28″ – $1,500.00 up.

In poor condition, redressed or original clothes in bad condition: 24″ – $300.00; 28″ – $450.00.
Clowns: Excellent condition: 18″ – $900.00; 26½″ – $1,800.00.

Poor condition: 18″ – $300.00; 26½″ – $500.00.
Indian or Oriental: In excellent, mint condition: 16″ – $1,000.00 up

Dirty and poor condition: 16″ – $300.00.
Golfer: Excellent, perfect condition: 16″ – $950.00.

Poor condition: 16″ – $200.00.
Shirley Temple Type: Excellent condition: 30″ – $1,200.00.

Poor condition: 30″ – $300.00.
Bali Dancer: Excellent condition: 22″ – $1,400.00.

Poor condition: 22″ – $300.00.

Smoking doll: In excellent condition, painted eyes: 25″ – $1,000.00.

In poor condition: 25″ – $350.00.

With glass eyes, in excellent condition: 16″ – $1,300.00; 20″ – $1,800.00 up.

Glass eyes: In poor condition: 16″ – $350.00; 20″ – $450.00.

14″ Lenci. All felt with all felt clothes. Marked Lenci on bottom of foot. 14″ – $650.00.

MASCOTTE. Mascotte dolls were made by May Freres Cie from 1890 to 1897, then this firm became part of Jules Steiner from 1898 into the 1900's. Some dolls are marked: Bebe Mascotte/Paris and others with an incised M-and a number. No damage to head or body and nicely dressed. Closed mouth. 16″ – $2,600.00; 18″ – $3,000.00; 20″ – $3,300.00; 22″ – $3,500.00; 24″ – $3,900.00.

16″ Bebe Mascotte. Closed mouth, paperweight eyes and on jointed composition body. Courtesy Kimport Dolls.

MECHANICALS

A. Theroude mechanical walker patented in 1840 with papier mache head with bamboo teeth in open mouth. Stands on three wheels, two large and one small, tin cart with mechanism attached to leg: 16″ – $1,600.00.

Autoperipatetikos of 1861. Base is clock like works and has tin feet and when wound the doll walks. Heads can be china, untinted bisque or papier mache: 11″ early china head – $1,100.00; 11″ later china hairdo – $825.00; 11″ untinted bisque head – $785.00; 11″ papier mache head – $550.00.

Hawkins, George walker with pewter hands and feet, wood torso. Hands modeled to push a carriage, which should be a Goodwin, patented in 1867-1868. Carriage has two large wheels and one small one in front. Molded hair, doll's head will be marked: X.L.C.R./Doll head/Pat. Sept. 8, 1868: 11″ – $1,400.00.

Jumeau: Raises and lowers both arms and head moves. Holds items such a hankie and bottle, book and fan, etc. one in each hand. Key wound music box in base. Closed mouth and marked Jumeau: 15″ – $3,000.00; 20″ – $3,800.00.

Same as above but with open mouth: 15″ – $1,600.00; 20″ – $2,600.00.

Jumeau: Marked Jumeau standing or sitting on music box that is key wound and doll plays an instrument: 14″ – $3,200.00; 17″ – $3,800.00.

Jumeau: Marked Jumeau walker with one piece leg, arms jointed at elbows and she raises her arm to blow kisses and the head turns. Cryer box and open mouth: 16″ – $1,400.00; 22″ – $2,000.00.

Jumeau: Marked Jumeau walker standing on three-wheel cart and when cart is pulled, the doll's head turns and arms go up and down: 15″ – $3,400.00; 18″ – $3,800.00.

Mid-1850's mechanical on music box that is key wound. Papier mache head with inset glass eyes, open mouth with bamboo teeth. Courtesy Barbara Earnshaw. 20″ – $4,800.00.

French mechanical that sits on key wound box and plays violin and head turns. Courtesy Barbara Earnshaw. 20″ – $3,800.00.

Steiner, Jules: Composition upper and lower torso-chest, also lower legs and all of arms. Twill covered sections of hips and upper legs. Key wound. Cries, kicks and turns head. Open mouth with two rows teeth. 18″ – $1,800.00.

Same as above but with bisque torso section: 18″ – $3,800.00.

All prices above are for originally dressed mechanicals and in working order. No damage to figure or any of the bisque parts. They will be a lot less if redressed or damaged in any way.

METAL DOLLS

Dolls marked Minerva were made by Buschow & Beck. Those marked Juno were made by Karl Standfuss and ones with a Diana mark were made by Alfred Heller. All are German. Marks:

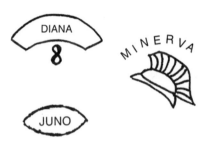

Doll with any of above marks: Can be on cloth or kid body and can have composition, celluloid or bisque lower arms. Many will be found on homemade bodies and these shoudl be well done and proportioned. Nicely dressed. Molded hair, glass eyes: 16″ – $100.00; 20″ – $145.00.

Molded hair, painted eyes: 12″ – $75.00; 16″ – $95.00; 20″ – $125.00.

Wigged and glass eyes: 16″ – $125.00; 20″ – $165.00.

All metal child: Nicely dressed, fully jointed, open or open/closed mouth and glass eyes: 17″ – $235.00; 20″ – $275.00.

All metal baby: Bent limb metal body (most are spring strung) molded hair and painted eyes. Nicely dressed. 12″ – $75.00; 16″ – $100.00; 18″ – $165.00.

14″ Brass shoulder head with the Minerva and helmet on front shoulder. Painted eyes and on kid body with bisque lower arms. Courtesy Shirley Pascuzzi. 14″ – $75.00.

NIPPON (JAPAN)

13″ Rare pouty closed mouth marked: Fy/Nippon/301. On toddler body and can also be on bent limb baby body. Sleep eyes. 13″ – $600.00.

At the outbreak of World War I, the German doll makers converted to wartime operations and Japan stepped into the doll void created. There were many obstacles for Japan to overcome in their attempt at molding and painting Western style dolls in the short time they were in production. (1918-1922). In the beginning their products were not too well done, but the quality of the dolls not only improved, but a few are excellent.

Morimura Brothers was the name of a very large Japanese import firm that imported dolls of all kinds from 1915 to 1922. In 1922, after World War I, their import section that handled dolls was taken over by Lanfelder, Homma & Hayward, Inc. Morimura Brothers mark:

Another major firm in Japan was Yamato and their marks are: **ꞯY**

The center for celluloid, metal and rubber dolls was Tokyo. Porcelain dolls were made in Kyoto; Osaka was where the dolls of cotton and paper were made.

Nippon marked baby: Good to excellent quality bisque, well painted, nice body with bent limbs and nicely dressed: 11" – $165.00; 15" – $225.00; 19" – $325.00; 24" – $495.00.

Nippon marked child: Good to excellent quality bisque, good fully jointed body, excellent quality painted features and nicely dressed: 16" – $245.00; 20" – $295.00; 24" – $350.00.

18" Marked: FY/Nippon/205. Bisque head with sleep eyes and open mouth. On bent limb baby body with jointed wrists. Courtesy Yesterday's Child. 18" – $300.00.

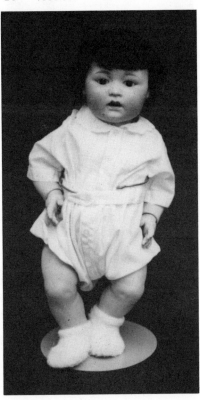

17" Bisque head baby made for Morimura Brothers Imports. Sleep eyes and open mouth with teeth. Courtesy Yesterday's Child. 17" – $265.00.

MOLDED HAIR BISQUE MOTSCHMANN

The molded hair bisques are just like any other flesh toned bisque dolls, but instead of having a wig, they have molded hair, glass set eyes and generally they will have a closed mouth. They almost always are a shoulder head with one-piece head and shoulder plate. They can be on kid body or cloth with bisque lower arms and some have composition lower legs. These dolls are generally very pretty.

Child: Girl: 16" – $395.00; 19" – $650.00; 21" – $875.00.

Boy: 16" – $500.00; 19" – $725.00; 21" – $950.00.

15" Bisque shoulder head with molded hair. Glass eyes, closed mouth and on kid body with bisque lower arms. Courtesy Kimport Dolls. 15" – $365.00.

13"-14" Bisque shoulder head girl with molded blonde hair. Set large glass eyes and closed mouth. Kid body with bisque lower arms. Courtesy Kimport Dolls. 13" – $300.00.

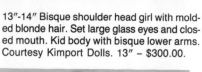

6" Motschmann style Oriental with painted papier mache head, lower arms and lower feet. Glass eyes. Cloth torso and upper arms and legs. Original clothes. 6" – $125.00.

Charles Motschmann made dolls from 1857 into 1960's in Sonneberg, Germany. These early dolls were babies, children and Orientals. They will have glass eyes, closed mouths and have heads of papier mache, wax over papier mache or wax over composition. They can have lightly brush stroke painted hair or come with a wig. If the mouth is open, they will have bamboo teeth. The larger dolls will have arms and legs jointed at the wrists and ankles. The torso (lower) is composition as are the arms and legs, except for the upper parts which will

be twill style cloth. The mid-section will also be cloth. If the doll is marked, it can be found on the upper cloth of the leg and will be stamped:

PATENT 29 APRIL
1857
CH. MOTSCHMANN
SONNEBERG

Motschmann marked or type baby: 14″ – $325.00; 17″ – $425.00; 21″ – $500.00; 25″ – $595.00.

ORSINI

Jeanne I. Orsini of New York City designed dolls from 1916 into the 1920's. It is not known who made the heads for her, but it is likely that all bisque dolls designed by her were made by J.D. Kestner in Germany. The initials of the designer are: J.I.O. and the dolls will be marked with these initials along with a year such as 1919, 1920, 1926, etc. Since the middle initial is I., it may appear to be a number 1. The dolls can also be marked: Copr. by/J.I.Orsini/Germany.

Painted bisque character: Can be on cloth body with cloth limbs or a bent limb baby body of composition, toddler or baby. Flirty sleep eyes and open smile mouth. Can be wigged or have molded hair and can be

boy or girl. Head is painted bisque. Mold #1429. Doll in excellent condition and well dressed: 14″ – $1,500.00; 18″ – $1,700.00.
Bisque head baby: Fired-in color bisque head with sleep or set eyes, open mouth. Cloth body and has painted hair. Marks: Kiddie Joy JIO 1926: 14″ – $1,150.00; 18″ – $1,800.00.
All bisque: Jointed at hips and shoulders with very character face, sleep eyes and painted on shoes and socks. Can be marked on back: Copy. by/J.I.Orsini/Germany, or have a paper label with doll's name on front. Names are DoDo, Fifi, Mimi, Didi, Zizi, etc.: 5″ – $1,200.00; 7″-8″ – $1,450.00.

18″ Painted bisque with flirty eyes and on all cloth body. Marks: Copr. by/J.I.Orsini/Germany. 18″ – $1,700.00 each.

PAPIER MACHE

Papier mache dolls were made in France, Germany, England, United States, and many other countries. Papier mache is a type of composition in that it is moldable-made from paper pulp, wood and rag fibers, containing paste, oil or glue. Flour, clay and/or sand was added for stiffness. The hardness of papier mache depends on the amount of glue that is added.

Many so called "papier mache" parts on dolls were actually laminated paper and not papier mache at all. Laminated paper doll heads/parts are several thicknesses of molded paper that have been bonded (glued) together, or pressed after being glued.

Papier mache means "chewed paper" in French, and as early as 1810, dolls of papier mache were being mass produced by using molds.

Marked: M&S Superior - 2015 (Muller & Strassburger): Papier mache shoulder head with blonde or black molded hair, painted blue or brown eyes, old cloth body with kid or leather arms and boots. Nicely dressed and head not repainted or chipped and cracked: 14″ – $175.00; 18″ – $250.00; 24″ – $350.00.

Repainted nicely: 14″ – $100.00; 18″ – $150.00; 24″ – $185.00.

Chips, scuffs or nor repainted very well: 14″ – $50.00; 18″ – $85.00; 24″ – $100.00.

French and French type: Painted black hair with brush marks on solid dome, some have nailed on wigs. Open mouth with bamboo teeth, inset glass eyes or full closed mouth. In very good condition (shows some wear), nice old clothes. All leather/kid body: 15″ – $625.00; 20″ – $1,000.00; 26″ – $1,500.00; 30″ – $2,000.00.

Early mache with cloth body and wooden limbs. Early hairdo with top knots, buns, puff curls or braiding. Ca. 1840's Not restored, in original or very old well made clothes. In very good condition and may

17″, 11″ and 5″ papier maches that are in excellent condition. Old clothes, cloth bodies with wooden limbs. 17″ size has a bun in back of molded hairdo and 11″ has braids. Courtesy Turn of Century Antiques. 5″ – $175.00; 11″ – $365.00; 17″ – $600.00.

18″ French papier mache. Ca. 1830. Black glass eyes, painted hair, cloth body with wooden arms and spoon hands. All originally dressed. Courtesy Pat Timmons. 18″ – $900.00.

show some extra wear: 10" – $350.00; 14" – $500.00; 17" – $600.00; 20" – $850.00; 24" – $1,200.00.

Marked Greiner dolls of 1858 on: Blonde or black molded hair, brown or blue painted eyes, cloth body with leather arms, nicely dressed and head not·repainted and with only very minor scuffs: 18" – $800.00; 23" – $1,100.00; 29" – $1,600.00; 32" – $1,900.00.

Motschmann types with wood and twill bodies. Separate torso section and separate hip section, glass eyes, closed mouth and brush stroke hair on solid dome. Nicely dressed and ready to display: 16" – $375.00; 20" – $485.00; 24" – $550.00.

German mache of 1870's-1900's with molded various curly hairdo, painted eyes and closed mouth. May be blonde or black hair. Nicely dressed and ready to display. Not repainted: 16" – $425.00; 20" – $500.00; 26" – $595.00; 32" – $800.00.

Turned shoulder head: Solid dome, glass eyes and closed mouth. Twill cloth body or kid body with composition lower arms. In very good condition, nicely dressed: 18" – $450.00; 22" – $700.00.

German character heads: These heads are modeled just like the bisque heads. Glass eyes, closed mouth and on fully jointed composition body. In excellent condition and nicely dressed: 16" – $650.00; 20" – $850.00.

1920's on mache: Papier mache head, usually with brighter colors than the older ones. Wigged, usually dressed as a child, or in Provincial costumes. Stuffed cloth bodies and limbs, or have mache arms/hands. In excellent overall condition: 12" – $85.00; 16" – $125.00.

Clowns: Papier mache head with clown painted features. Open or closed mouth, molded hair or wigged and on cloth body with some having composition or papier mache lower arms: In excellent condition: 12" – $250.00; 16" – $400.00.

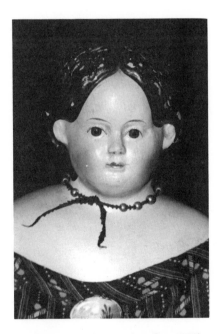

21" German papier mache. Ca. 1850's. Molded hair and painted features. Cloth body with leather arms. Courtesy Helen Draves. 21" – $650.00.

13" Papier mache of 1840's. Cloth body with wooden limbs. Courtesy Kimport Dolls. 13" – $595.00.

PAPIER MACHE

18" Smiling papier mache with cloth body and composition arms and legs. Glass eyes and open/closed mouth with two painted lower teeth. Courtesy Jane Walker. 18" – $295.00.

14" Papier mache shoulder head made by Muller & Strassburger and marked: M & S Superior 2015. Cloth body with leather hands and sewn on stockings and boots. Courtesy Jay Minter. 14" – $175.00.

German papier mache head with glass eyes, closed mouth and wig. Would be on cloth body with leather arms. Courtesy Kathy Walters. 26" – $595.00.

5" Tall German papier mache head with molded hair and painted features. Should have cloth body with cloth or leather arms. Courtesy Helen Draves. 20" – $500.00.

PARIAN-TYPE (UNTINTED BISQUE)

The use of the name "Parian" is incorrect for dolls, but the term has been used for so long it would be difficult to attempt to change it. The dolls are actually made of unglazed porcelain.

"Parian-type" dolls were made from the 1850's to the 1880's with the majority being made in the 1870's and 1880's. All seemed to have been made in Germany and if marked, the mark will be found on the inside of the shoulder plate. As to variety, there are hundreds of different heads and an entire collection could be made up of them. It must be noted that the really rare and unique unglazed porcelain dolls are difficult to find and their prices will be high.

"Parian-type" dolls can be found with every imaginable thing applied to heads and shirt tops, from flowers, snoods, ruffles, feathers, plumes, ribbons, etc. Many have inset glass eyes, pierced ears and most are blondes, although some will have light to medium brown hair and a few will have glazed black hair.

Some of the "parian-type" unglazed porcelain dolls and China dolls shared the same molds, and the men and boys as well as ones with swivel necks can be considered rare.

Various fancy hairstyles: With modeled combs, ribbons, flowers, head bands or snoods. Cloth body with cloth/"parian" limbs. Perfect condition and very nicely dressed: Glass eyes, pierced ears: 17" – $1,250.00 up; 21" – $1,450.00 up.

Painted eyes, unpierced ears: 17" – $750.00 up; 21" – $900.00 up.

Modeled necklaces, jewels or standing ruffles (undamaged): Glass eyes, pierced ears: 17" – $1,250.00 up; 21" – $1,500.00 up.

Painted eyes, unpierced ears: 17" – $700.00; 21" – $1,000.00.

22" Glass eye "parian" with dark blonde wide curls. Pierced ears and decorated shoulder plate. Cloth body with "parian" arms. 22" – $1,500.00.

19" "Parian" with applied wreath of Dresden style flowers in molded hair and also has blue luster ribbon with tassel. Cloth body with parian limbs. Courtesy Kimport Dolls. 19" – $895.00.

PARIAN-TYPE (UNTINTED BISQUE)

Bald Head: Solid domes that takes wigs, full ear detail. 1850's. Perfect condition and nicely dressed: 14″ – $500.00; 16″ – $695.00; 20″ – $1,100.00.

Very plain style with no decoration in hair or on shoulder. No damage and nicely dressed: 15″ – $200.00; 18″ – $325.00.

Men or boys: Men or boy hairdos with center or side parts. Cloth body with cloth/parian limbs. Decorated shirt and tie: 15″ – $400.00; 18″ – $750.00.

Undecorated shirt top: 15″ – $350.00; 18″ – $700.00.

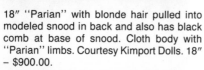

19½″ "Parian" with pierced ears, blonde molded hair with decoration. Cloth body with "Parian" lower arms. Courtesy Kimport Dolls. 19½″ – $900.00.

18″ "Parian" with blonde hair pulled into modeled snood in back and also has black comb at base of snood. Cloth body with "Parian" limbs. Courtesy Kimport Dolls. 18″ – $900.00.

20″ "Countess Dagmar" of 1870's. White skin tones with very pale blonde molded hair. Modeled on shirtwaist top. Painted blue enamel eyes. Courtesy Kimport Dolls. 20″ – $850.00.

PARIAN-TYPE (UNTINTED BISQUE)

17" White bisque with long blonde molded hair, kid body with kid limbs and sewn on boots. Ears are fully exposed. Mark:974 ✗ 7. 17" – $565.00.

17" "Parian" man and lady. Both have modeled shirt fronts and tie/bow. Both have very light brown molded hair and painted features. Cloth bodies with "parian" limbs. Courtesy Verna Humphrey. 17" man – $725.00; 17" woman – $725.00.

21" "Parian" with center part blonde molded hair and painted features. Cloth body with "parian" limbs. Many of the "parian" style dolls were also made in China and this is an example of one of them. Courtesy Kimport Dolls. 21" – $565.00.

PARIS BEBE
PARSONS-JACKSON

PARIS BEBE. Dolls marked with Paris Bebe were made by Danel & Cie in France from 1889 to 1895. The heads will be marked: Paris Bebe/Tete Depose or Tete Depose/Paris Bebe. The bodies will be marked with an Eiffel Tower/Paris Bebe/Brevete.

Paris Bebe Child: Bisque head, closed mouth, glass eyes and on composition jointed body. No damage, clean and nicely dressed: 16" – $2,600.00; 20" – $3,100.00; 24" – $3,600.00.

16½" Bisque head marked: Paris Bebe/Tete Depose and has the tower stamp on body, which is a fully jointed composition. Courtesy Kimport Dolls. 16½" – $2,600.00.

PARSONS-JACKSON

Parsons-Jackson Company operated from 1910 to 1919 in Cleveland, Ohio, and used a material called biskoline. Generally their dolls are spring (metal) strung and the trademark from this company is a stork along with the name of the firm: Marks:

PARSONS-JACKSON CO.
CLEVELAND, OHIO

TRADE MARK

Baby: Bent limb baby body, painted hair and eyes and all biskoline (similar to heavy celluloid). Nicely dressed and in excellent condition: 10" – $100.00; 12"-13" – $165.00.

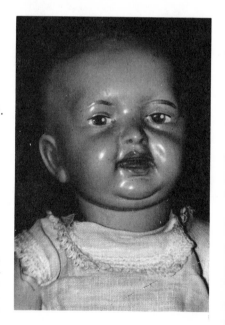

10" Baby made of biskoline with bent limb baby body. Painted hair and eyes. Open/closed mouth. Marks: picture of stork/Trademark/Parsons-Jackson/Cleveland/Oh. Ca. 1910. Courtesy Kimport Dolls. 10" – $100.00.

PETIT & DUMONTIER. Petit & Dumontier made dolls in France from 1878 to 1890. They have bisque heads and composition bodies with metal hands. The mark will be: P.D., along with a size number. Courtesy Barbara Earnshaw.

P.D. Child: METAL HANDS, composition jointed body, bisque head with closed mouth and paperweight eyes. Nicely dressed and wigged and ready to display: 16″ – $3,200.00; 22″ – $4,000.00; 26″ – $5,600.00.

16″ Marked: P.D. on head. Closed mouth and has metal hands. Courtesy Barbara Earnshaw. 16″ – $3,200.00.

RABERY & DELPHIEU

Rabery & Delphieu began making dolls in 1856. The very first dolls had kid bodies and are extremely rare. The majority of the Rabery & Delphieu dolls are on French composition/wood or mache bodies. They will be marked with: R.D. A few may be marked: Bebe Rabery or Bebe de Paris.

Child with closed mouth: In excellent condition with no chips, breaks or hairlines to the bisque head. Body in overall good condition, dressed and wigged and ready to place into a collection: 14″ – $1,700.00; 17″ – $2,000.00; 20″ – $2,600.00; 22″ – $2,800.00; 25″ – $3,100.00.

Child with open mouth: Same condition as stated for closed mouth dolls: 14″ – $900.00; 17″ – $1,600.00; 20″ – $1,900.00; 22″ – $2,000.00; 25″ – $2,400.00.

27″ Marked: R.D. Closed mouth and large paperweight eyes. Excellent quality bisque, nicely dressed and wigged. On French jointed composition body. Courtesy Barbara Earnshaw. 27″ – $3,500.00.

RECHNAGEL OF ALEXANDERINETHAL

Dolls marked with an R.A. were made by Rechnagel of Alexanderinethal, Thur, Germany. They came also marked with a number and/or Germany. These dolls have a bisque head, composition bodies, as well as papier mache and wood jointed bodies. R.A. marked dolls date from 1886 to after World War I and can range from excellent workmanship to very poor workmanship. Prices shown are for dolls with good artist painting (lips painted straight as well as the eyebrows), nicely or originally dressed and no damage to head nor body.

Child: Set or sleep eyes, open mouth with small dolls having painted-on shoes/socks: 7"-8" – $100.00; 12" – $165.00; 15" – $235.00; 19" – $325.00; 21" – $425.00.

Baby: Ca. 1909-1910 on. Five-piece bent limb baby body or straight leg, curved arm toddler body and with sleep or set eyes, open mouth. No damage to head or body and nicely dressed: 9" – $125.00; 12" – $185.00; 16" – $250.00; 19" – $325.00.

Character: With painted eyes, modeled on bonnet and open/closed mouth, some with painted in teeth. Not damaged and nicely dressed: 8" – $475.00; 12" – $545.00.

Character: Glass eyes, closed mouth and composition bent limb baby body: 7" – $495.00; 10" – $550.00; 13" – $695.00.

6" Marked R.A. Five-piece papier mache body covered with fur and bisque head also covered with fur. Sleep eyes and open mouth. The Youth's Companion magazine of 1894 shows this style as "Yukla", an Eskimo doll which was used as a premium. The dolls gained further popularity when Admiral Perry discovered the North Pole. Courtesy Shirley Pascuzzi. 6" – $100.00.

Dolls marked with a P.M. were made by Otto Reinecke of Hof-Moschendorf, Bavaria, Germany, from 1909 into the 1930's. The most often found mold number from this company is the 914 baby or toddler. The marks include the P.M. as well as a number and/or Germany.

Child: Bisque head, open mouth and on five-piece papier mache body or jointed body. Can have set or sleep eyes. No damage to head or body, nicely dressed and ready to display: 9″ – $125.00; 12″ – $195.00; 15″ – $285.00; 18″ – $375.00; 22″ – $450.00.

Baby: Open mouth and sleep or set eyes. Bisque head on five-piece bent limb baby body. No damage and nicely dressed: 12″ – $250.00; 16″ – $375.00; 22″ – $500.00; 25″ – $675.00.

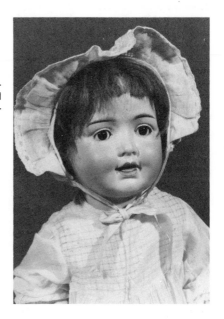

22″ Marked: P.M/924. Bisque head on five-piece bent limb baby body. Open mouth and sleep eyes. Molded tongue. Courtesy Kimport Dolls. 22″ – $500.00.

21″ Marked: P.M./914 with bisque head, open mouth and sleep eyes. Five-piece bent limb baby body. Courtesy Yesterday's Child. 21″ – $495.00.

REVALO
SCHMIDT, FRANZ

The Revalo marked dolls were made by Gebruder Ohlhaver of Thur, Germany in 1921 into the 1930's. Bisque heads on composition bodies.

Children: Sleep or set eyes, open mouth and bisque heads on jointed bodies. Not damaged and nicely dressed: 14″ – $350.00; 17″ – $450.00; 20″ – $525.00; 24″ – $600.00.

Character baby: Bisque head with open mouth, sleep or set eyes. Five-piece bent limb baby body. No damage and nicely dressed: 15″ – $450.00; 17″ – $550.00.

Toddler body: 15″ – $500.00; 17″ – $600.00.

Molded hair child: Molded hair with or without molded ribbon and/or flowers. Painted eyes and open/closed mouth. Jointed composition body. No damage, breaks or chips and nicely dressed: 11″ – $565.00; 14″ – $695.00.

14″ Marked: Revalo/22-4. Bisque head with open mouth and sleep eyes. Five-piece bent limb baby body. Courtesy Yesterday's Child. 14″ – $450.00.

SCHMIDT, FRANZ

Franz Schmidt & Co. began in 1890 at Georgenthal, near Walterhausen, Thur. They obtained an extremely interesting patent (in England) during 1891 for sleeping eyes made so the upper lids moved further and faster than the lower lids. It was in 1902 they registered the trademarks of crossed hammers with a doll between and the "F.S.&Co." mark.

Baby: Bisque head on bent limb baby body. Sleep or set eyes, open mouth and some may have pierced nostrils. Not damaged in any way and nicely dressed: Mold #1272: 14″ – $425.00; 17″ – $525.00; 20″ – $645.00; 24″ – $825.00. Mold #1285: 16″ – $500.00; 20″ – $600.00. Mold #1295, #1296: 14″ – $400.00; 17″ – $475.00; 20″ – $575.00; 24″ – $775.00. **Add more for toddler body.**

Child: Mache and composition body with walker mechanism with metal rollers on feet. Open mouth and sleep eyes. Working and no damage to head nor body. Mold #1250: 12″ – $195.00; 16″ – $525.00; 20″ – $650.00.

Marked 15″ baby: F.S.& C. Open/closed mouth with sleep eyes and all original clothes and wig. On five-piece bent limb baby body. 15″ – $450.00.

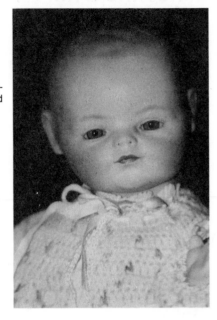

16″ Marked: F.S.& C./1285 baby with five-piece bent limb baby body. Sleep eyes and closed mouth. 16″ – $500.00.

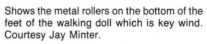

16″ Marked: 2/F.S & C/1250/30. Walker body, open mouth and sleep eyes. All original. Courtesy Jay Minter. 16″ – $525.00.

Shows the metal rollers on the bottom of the feet of the walking doll which is key wind. Courtesy Jay Minter.

SCHMITT & FILS
SCHOENAU & HOFFMEISTER

Schmitt & Fils produced dolls from 1870's to 1891 in Paris, France. They should be marked on head and body with crossed hammers in a shield. They have composition/wood jointed bodies and came with fully closed mouths or open/closed mouths. Marks:

Child: Bisque head on jointed composition/wood body with closed mouth or open/closed mouth. No damage, chips or hairlines and body in excellent condition. Dressed nicely in the French styles and ready to display: 15″ – $3,200.00; 18″ – $5,200.00; 20″ – $5,500.00; 23″ – $5,900.00; 25″ – $6,300.00.

18″ Marked on head and body: crossed hammers in shield. Large paperweight eyes and closed mouth. On Schmitt jointed composition body. Courtesy Barbara Earnshaw. 18″ # $5,200.00.

SCHOENAU & HOFFMEISTER

Schoenau & Hoffmeister began making dolls in 1901 and were located in Bavaria. The factory was called "Porzellanfabrik Burgrubb" and this mark will be found on some dolls' heads. Dolls are also marked with a five-point star with the initials SH and a pb inside the star. Some of their mold numbers are: 21, 169, 170, 769, 900, 914, 1800, 1906, 1909, 1923, 4000, 4500, 4900, 5000, 5300, 5500, 5700, 5800, Hanna. Mark:

Oriental: Mold #4900. Open mouth, sleep or set eyes. Bisque head on jointed olive toned composition body. No damage and nicely dressed in Oriental styles: 10″ – $365.00; 14″ – $895.00; 18″ – $1,300.00.
Princess Elizabeth: Smiling open mouth, sleep eyes and on chubby five-piece composition body. Marked with name on head. No damage to head or body: 16″ – $2,300.00; 20″ – $2,700.00; 24″ – $3,400.00.
Hanna: Brown or Black bisque (fired-in color), open mouth papier mache five-piece or jointed body. Sleep or set eyes. No damage and dressed in grass skirt or native print cloth gown: 8″ – $185.00; 10″ – $250.00.
Hanna Baby: Character head of bisque with open mouth and sleep eyes. On five-piece bent limb baby body. No damage and nicely dressed: 17″ – $595.00; 24″ – $895.00.
Character Baby: Bisque head on five-piece bent limb baby baody. Open mouth and set or sleep eyes. No damage and nicely dressed: 12″ – $300.00; 17″ – $525.00; 20″ – $600.00; 24″ – $700.00.
Character Toddler: Same description as babies but with a toddler body: 17″ – $625.00; 20″ – $700.00.

Children: Bisque head with open mouth and set or sleep eyes, composition jointed body. No damage to head or body and nicely dressed ready to go into a collection: 10" – $100.00; 15" – $285.00; 18" – $350.00; 21" – $425.00; 26" – $600.00; 30" – $950.00.

30½" Marked with S, pb, in star, H. Bisque head with sleep eyes and hair lashes, open mouth and on jointed composition body. Courtesy Kimport Dolls. 30½" – $950.00.

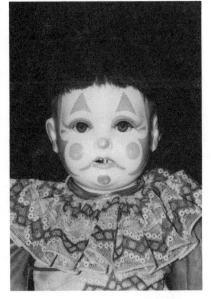

26½" Painted bisque clown. Sleep eyes with hair lashes, open mouth and marked: S PB, in star H./170-4/Germany. On jointed composition body. Courtesy Kimport Dolls. 26½" – $750.00.

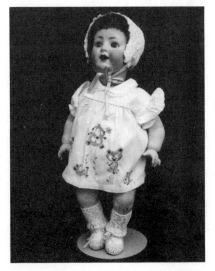

24" Marked: Porzellanfabrik Burgrubb/-169-5½. On five-piece toddler body. Sleep eyes and open mouth. Courtesy Yesterday's Child. 24" – $700.00.

SCHOENHUT

The Albert Schoenhut & Co. was located in Philadelphia, Pa. from 1872 into 1930's. Albert's grandfather and father were both wood carvers in Germany. It was in 1909 that Albert applied for a patent for a swivel spring-jointed doll, but did not receive the patent until 1911. It was in 1913 that he began making the infant doll with bent limbs. In 1924 the Schoenhut firm bought out the "Bass Wood Elastic Dolls" that were jointed by elastic instead of springs and were cheaper in price. Schoenhut dolls will be incised: Schoenhut Doll/Pat. Jan. 17, '11. U.S.A./& foreign countries and will have a paper label with the same mark in an oval.

Child with molded hair: May have comb marks, molded ribbon, comb or bow. Closed mouth and spring-jointed all wood. Original or nice clothes: Excellent condition: 16″ – $1,150.00; 19″ – $1,375.00.

Very good condition with some wear: 16″ – $700.00; 19″ – $850.00.

Poor condition with chips and dents: 16″ – $400.00; 19″ – $500.00.

Baby head: Can be on regular body or bent limb baby body. Bald spray painted hair or wig, painted decal eyes and all wood: Nicely dressed: Excellent condition: 16″ – $525.00; 17″ – $595.00.

Good condition: 16″ – $350.00; 17″ – $395.00.

Poor condition: 16″ – $200.00; 17″ – $225.00.

"Dolly" face, common doll: Wigged, open/closed mouth with painted teeth, decal painted eyes and spring-jointed. Original or nicely dressed: Excellent condition: 17″ – $385.00; 20″ – $495.00.

Good condition: 17″ – $200.00; 20″ – $250.00.

Poor condition: 17″ – $150.00; 20″ – $195.00.

Sleep eyes: Has lids that lower down over the eyes and has an open mouth with teeth or just slightly cut open with carved teeth. Original or nicely dressed: Excellent condition: 17″ – $700.00; 20″ – $850.00.

Good condition: 17″ – $350.00; 20″ – $450.00.

Poor condition: 17″ – $200.00; 20″ – $265.00.

Walker: All wood with one-piece legs with "walker" joints in center of legs and torso. Painted decal eyes and closed or open/closed mouth. Original or nicely dressed: Excellent condition: 17″ – $695.00; 20″ – $895.00.

Good condition: 17″ – $325.00; 20″ – $425.00.

Poor condition: 17″ – $175.00; 20″ – $225.00.

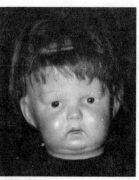

17″ Schoenhut baby. All wood with Schoenhut seal on body. Body is a five-piece bent limb baby body and eyes are decals. Courtesy Helen Draves. 17″ – $525.00.

16″ "Dolly style" face Schoenhut with open/closed mouth and painted teeth. Eyes are brown decals. Original wig. Courtesy Helen Draves. 16″ – $225.00.

Schuetzmeister & Quendt only made dolls for a few short years from 1893 to 1898. The factory was located in Boilstat,Thur, Germany. Some of their mold numbers are: 101, 201, 301. Marks:

Child: Can have cut pate or be a bald head with two stringing holes. No damage and nicely dressed, open mouth: 16" – $400.00; 20" – $500.00; 24" – $600.00.

Baby: Five-piece bent limb body. Not damaged and nicely dressed. Open mouth: 14" – $325.00; 17" – $425.00; 22" – $625.00.

SQ SQ S
              Q

20½" Marked: S Q 201. Bisque head with sleep eyes and open mouth. On five-piece bent limb baby body. Courtesy Yesterday's Child.

9" Bald head with two stringing holes. Solid jointed composition body. Closed mouth and marked: SQ 20. In original trunk with wardrobe. Courtesy Kimport Dolls. 9" – $465.00.

SIMON & HALBIG

Simon & Halbig made some of the finest German dolls manufactured. They began making dolls sometime in the late 1860's or early 1870's and continued until the 1930's. Simon & Halbig made a great many heads for almost all the major doll makers of their time. They also supplied heads for the French trade. They made entire dolls, all bisque, flange necked dolls, turned shoulder heads and socket heads.

In 1895 Simon left the firm (retired or deceased) and Carl Halbig took over as single owner. Their dolls are marked with the full name or just the initials: S.H. or S.&H.

All prices are for dolls with no damage to the bisque heads and only minor scuffs to the bodies. They are well dressed, wigged and have shoes. These dolls should be ready to place into a collection.

SIMON & HALBIG

Child: Open mouth and composition body. #719, 939, 949: 16″ – $750.00; 20″ – $950.00; 25″ – $1,200.00.

#130, 540, 550, 1009, 1039, 1040, 1078, 1079, etc.: Allow extra for flirty eyes: 12″ – $325.00; 15″ – $385.00; 18″ – $495.00; 22″ – $585.00; 26″ – $700.00; 30″ – $950.00; 36″ – $1,500.00.

Child: Open mouth and kid body. #1009 with fashion style kid body: 18″ – $525.00; 23″ – $725.00.

#1010, 1040, 1080, etc.: 16″ – $350.00; 21″ – $495.00; 25″ – $625.00.

#1250, 1260: 15″ – $325.00; 18″ – $425.00; 21″ – $500.00; 24″ – $600.00. **Characters:** Wig or molded hair, glass or painted eyes and with open, closed or open/closed mouths. On jointed compositon body: #120: 14″ – $1,200.00; 22″ – $2,300.00.

#150: 18″ – $7,900.00; 22″ – $8,400.00.

#151: 16″ – $5,000.00; 22″ – $7,800.00.

#153: 16″ – $5,000.00.

#600: 14″ – $425.00; 18″ – $765.00.

#718, 719: 16″ – $1,800.00; 20″ – $2,200.00.

#740: 16″ – $1,200.00; 20″ – $1,600.00.

#905, 908: 14″ – $1,600.00; 17″ – $2,600.00.

#939, Composition body: 17″ – $1,800.00; 20″ – $2,200.00; 25″ – $2,800.00.

#949: 17″ – $1,300.00; 20″ – $1,600.00; 25″ – $2,300.00.

#939, Kid body: 17″ – $1,600.00; 20″ – $2,000.00; 25″ – $2,600.00.

#949: 17″ – $1,100.00; 20″ – $1,500.00; 25″ – $2,100.00.

#939, Composition body. Black: 17″ – $2,200.00; 20″ – $2,600.00.

#949: 17″ – $1,700.00; 20″ – $2,000.00.

#950, Kid body: 10″ – $465.00; 14″ – $600.00.

#1249 Santa: 16″ – $725.00; 20″ – $895.00; 26″ – $1,000.00.

#1279: 16″ – $995.00; 21″ – $1,600.00; 25″ – $2,000.00; 30″ – $3,000.00.

#1299: 17″ – $900.00; 21″ – $1,000.00.

#1358, Black doll: 17″ – $4,500.00; 21″ – $5,400.00; 24″ – $6,000.00.

#1388, Lady doll: 21″ – $7,600.00; 26″ – $12,000.00.

#1428: 20″ – $1,600.00.

#1478: 16″ – $3,500.00.

#1488: 16″ – $2,000.00; 20″ – $3,900.00. **Character Babies:** Wigs, or molded hair, painted or sleep eyes, open or open/closed mouths and on five-piece bent limb baby body or toddler body: #1294: 15″ – $525.00; 18″ – $625.00; 22″ – $725.00; 25″ – $850.00.

#1294 with clockwork mechanism in head: 25″-26″ – $2,000.00.

#1428, Toddler: 12″ – $1,250.00; 16″ – $1,450.00; 20″ – $1,850.00.

#1428, Baby: 12″ – $800.00; 16″ – $1,100.00; 20″ – $1,500.00.

#1488, Toddler: 17″ – $3,200.00; 20″ – $3,600.00; 24″ – $.   .

#1488, Baby: 17″ – $1,900.00; 20″ – $2,100.00; 24″ – $.   .

#1489, Ericka: 19″ – $1,800.00; 25″ – $3,000.00.

#1498, Toddler: 16″ – $2,000.00; 20″ – $3,600.00.

#1498, Baby: 16″ – $1,400.00; 20″ – $2,400.00.

Walker: Key wound: #1039: 16″ – $995.00; 20″ – $1,400.00.

#1039 Walking and kissing doll: 18″ – $750.00; 22″ – $995.00.

Miniature Dolls: Tiny doll with open mouth on composition jointed or five-piece body with some having painted-on shoes and socks: Fully jointed body: 8″ – $345.00; 10″ – $425.00.

Five-piece body: 8″ – $245.00; 10″ – $325.00.

Little Women type: Closed mouth and fancy wig: #1160: 6″ – $300.00; 9″ – $375.00.

Ladies: Open mouths, molded lady style body, slim arms and legs: #1159, 1179: 18″

– $1,500.00; 22″ – $1,800.00; 25″ – $2,200.00.

Ladies: With closed mouths, slim limbs and adult style composition body: #1303: 15″ – $3,800.00; 18″ – $5,400.00.

#1469: 15″ – $1,400.00; 18″ – $2,600.00.

26″ Marked: 939/Simon & Halbig. Bisque head with large paperweight set eyes, open/closed mouth with white area between lips. On fully jointed composition body. 26″ – $2,800.00.

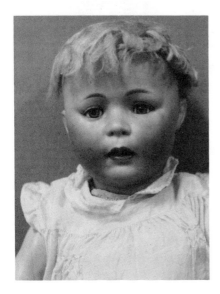

28″ Marked: 1488 S & H. Bisque head with sleep eyes and wide open/closed mouth. On five-piece bent limb body. Original wig. Courtesy Mrs. Nolte. 28″ – $4,400.00.

16″ Marked: S 7 H/908. Paperweight eyes, open mouth with two upper teeth. Jointed body with straight wrists. Courtesy Jay Minter. 16″ – $2,200.00.

SIMON & HALBIG

31″ Marked: S & H/ Santa 1249/Germany. Open mouth with sleep eyes and molded eyebrows. Jointed composition body. Courtesy Kimport Dolls. 31″ – $2,000.00.

15″ Simon & Halbig Oriental with olive skin tones, sleep eyes and on jointed olive tone marked Halbig body. "Mama and Papa" voice box in body with two pull strings. Maybe original wig and clothes. Courtesy Turn of Century Antiques. 15″ – $2,200.00.

22″ Marked: S & H/1039. Walker with straight walker legs and jointed arms. Open mouth with upper teeth and flirty eyes with hair lashes. Courtesy Jay Minter. 22″ – $1,600.00.

23" Simon & Halbig/1159/Germany. On composition jointed adult body with slim limbs. Courtesy Turn of Century Antiques. 23" – $2,100.00.

14" Flapper marked: S & H/1159/6/Germany. Sleep eyes, open mouth and has slender body with knees jointed high above knee to allow for short styles of clothes. Original hat and wig. Re-dressed by owner. Courtesy Gloyra Woods. 14" – $1,200.00.

All marked S & H 1160 and referred to as "Little Women". All have original wigs. Left to right: head sizes: 2½", 1½" and 3". Courtesy Turn of Century Antiques. 6" – $300.00; 9" – $375.00.

SIMON & HALBIG
S.F.B.J.

Left to right: 17″, 11½″ and 34″ with all marked: S & H 1009. All have open mouths and glass eyes. Two larger ones on composition jointed bodies and small one is shoulder head on kid body with bisque lower arms. Courtesy Turn of Century Antiques. 11½″ – $325.00; 17″ – $450.00; 34″ – $1,400.00.

18″ Marked: 570/Germany/Halbig/S & H. Open mouth, sleep eyes and only fully jointed composition body. 18″ – $495.00.

S.F.B.J.

The Societe Francaise de Fabrication de Bebes et Jouets (S.F.B.J.) was formed in 1899 and known members were Jumeau, Bru, Fleischmann & Blodel, Rabery & Delphieu, Pintel & Godchaux, P.H. Schmitz, A. Bouchet, Jullien and Danel & Cie.

The director was Fleischmann and at the beginning of World War I, he was deported and his properties taken from him because he was an alien (Germany). By 1922 S.F.B.J. employed 2,800 people. The Society dissolved in the mid-1950's.

There are a vast amount of "dolly" faced S.F.B.J. dolls, but also some are extremely rare and are character molds. Most of the character dolls are in the 200 series of mold numbers. Marks:

**S.F.B.J.
239
PARIS**

Child: Sleep or set eyes, open mouth and on jointed composition body. No damage and nicely dressed in the French style. #60: 14″ – $465.00; 20″ – $625.00; 24″ – $785.00.

#301: 8″ – $195.00; 14″ – $565.00; 18″ – $785.00; 22″ – $895.00; 28″ – $1,100.00; 32″ – $1,500.00.

Jumeau-type: 16″ – $900.00; 20″ – $1,150.00; 24″ – $1,600.00; 28″ – $2,000.00.

Closed mouth: 16″ – $1,200.00; 20″ – $1,600.00; 24″ – $2,000.00; 28″ – $2,400.00.

Character: Sleep or set eyes, wigged or with molded hair and some may have flocked hair over molded. Composition body. Nicely dressed and ready to display. No damage at all to head and only minor scuffs to body: #211: 16″ – $4,700.00.

#226: 16″ – $1,700.00; 21″ – $1,900.00.

#227: 16″ – $1,800.00; 21″ – $2,000.00.

#230: 23″ – $1,600.00.

#233: 14″ – $1,600.00; 17″ – $3,000.00.

#234: 16″ – $2,550.00; 21″ – $2,950.00.

#235: 16″ – $1,700.00; 21″ – $1,900.00.

#236: Toddlers: 12″ – $1,200.00; 16″ – $1,600.00; 20″ – $2,000.00; 25″ – $2,500.00.

#236: Baby: 16″ – $1,300.00; 21″ – $1,700.00.

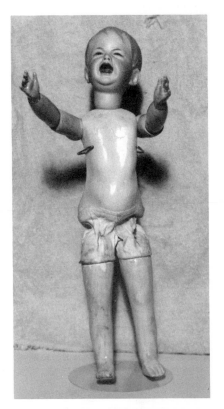

Body of #233 Mold "Screamer". Composition with leather torso and upper legs. Cryer works when legs are moved back and forth. Has cut out in back with wire screen cover for sound to escape. Courtesy Turn of Century Antiques.

#237: 16″ – $1,700.00; 21″ – $1,900.00.

#238: 16″ – $2,500.00; 21″ – $2,900.00.

#239 (Poubout): 14″ – $3,700.00; 17″ – $4,300.00.

#242: 17″ – $3,200.00.

#247: 16″ – $1,700.00; 21″ – $2,500.00.

#251: Toddler: 16″ – $1,700.00; 20″ – $2,000.00; 26″ – $2,500.00. Baby: 10″ – $895.00; 16″ – $1,300.00; 21″ – $1,600.00.

#252: Toddler: 16″ – $3,500.00; 20″ – $5,000.00; 26″ – $7,000.00. Baby: 10″ – $2,000.00; 16″ – $2,400.00.

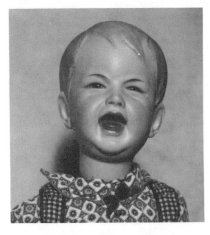

22″ "Screamer" Marked: S.F.B.J. 233. Squinted glass eyes and wide open/closed mouth and deeply molded hair. Composition body with straight legs and leather torso to house cryer mechanism as legs are moved. Courtesy Turn of Century Antiques. 22″ – $3,800.00.

S.F.B.J.

#257: 16″ – $1,800.00.

#266: 20″ – $1,700.00.

Googly: Mold #245. No damage and nicely dressed: 14″-15″ – $5,000.00.

Kiss-throwing & walking doll: Composition body with straight legs, walking mechanism and when walks, arm goes up to throw kiss. Head moves from side to side. Flirty eyes and open mouth. In working condition, not damaged, bisque head without any damage, nicely dressed in French styles and ready to display: 21″-22″ – $1,500.00.

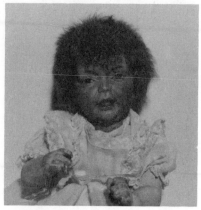

28″ S.F.B.J. 226 with brush stroke hair, paperweight eyes and wide open/closed mouth. Two pull strings on side of body for voice box. Courtesy Turn of Century Antiques. 28″ – $2,600.00.

15″ Marked: S.F.B.J. 226 with glass eyes, open/closed mouth and caracul wig. On five-piece bent limb baby body. Courtesy Turn of Century Antiques. 15″ – $1,600.00.

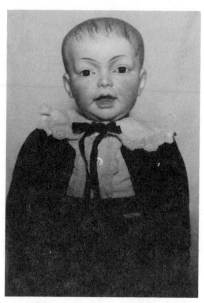

17″ Marked S.F.B.J. 235 with molded hair, glass eyes, open/closed mouth with molded upper teeth. On jointed composition body. Courtesy Barbara Earnshaw. 17″ – $1,700.00.

15½″ Marked: S.F.B.J. 229 with set paperweight eyes, open/closed mouth with modeled upper teeth and on a jointed toddler body. Courtesy Kimport Dolls. 15½″ – $1,700.00.

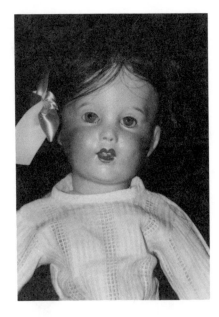

16″ Marked: S.F.B.J. 251. Sleep eyes, open/closed mouth with upper teeth and on fully jointed body. Courtesy Kimport Dolls. 16″ – $1,300.00.

13″ S.F.B.J. 236 with S.F.B.J. marked body. Open/closed mouth with two molded upper teeth. On jointed toddler body. Courtesy Jay Minter. 13″ – $1,300.00.

S.F.B.J.

22″ Early marked: S.F.B.J. Depose. Walker and throws kisses. Open mouth, set eyes with hair lashes and feathered painted brows. Courtesy Turn of Century Antiques. 22″ – $1,500.00.

21″ Walking, kissing marked: France/-S.F.B.J. Has sleep eyes with hair lashes and heavy painted lashes below eyes. Open mouth. When she walks her arm comes up to blow a kiss. Courtesy Jay Minter. 21″ – $1,500.00.

15″ Marked: S.F.B.J./301/Paris. Open mouth and on fully jointed compositon body. Courtesy Jay Minter. 15″ – $595.00.

Snow Babies were made both in Germany and Japan and can be of excellent to very poor in quality from both countries. Snow Babies have a "pebbles" covering fired-on like clothes. Many are unmarked. The features are painted:
Single figure: 1½" – $55.00; 3" – $100.00.
Two figures together: 1½" – $125.00; 3" – $195.00.
Three figures together: 1½" – $175.00; 3" – $225.00.
One figure on sled: 2"-2½" – $125.00.
Two figures on sled: 2"-2½" – $145.00.
Three figures on sled: 3" – $165.00; 6" – $200.00.

Jointed shoulders and hips: 5" – $300.00.
Shoulder head, cloth body and china limbs: 7"-9" – $350.00.
Rare Snow Babies: On sled in glass "snow scene": $145.00.

With bear: $165.00.

Musical base: $125.00 up.

With snowman: 3" – $150.00.

Laughing child: 3" – $95.00.

Snow Bear with Santa: $250.00.

With reindeer: $125.00.

SKOOKUM INDIAN DOLLS

Face mask with wig, wool blanket forms body that is stuffed with twigs and leaves or grass. Wood dowel legs and wooden feet. Paper label on feet. 4" – $18.00; 6" – $25.00; 12" – $55.00; 15" – $95.00; 18" – $135.00; 22" – $185.00; 30" – $300.00; 36" – $595.00.
Squaw with baby: 15" – $125.00; 18" – $200.00; 22" – $325.00.
Portrait Chief: 15" – $125.00; 18" – $200.00; 22" – $325.00.
Sitting Squaw: 8" – $100.00.

STEINER, JULES

Jules Nichols Steiner operated from 1855 to 1892 when the firm was taken over by Amedee LaFosse. In 1895 this firm merged with Henri Alexander (maker of Bebe Phenix) and May Freres Cie (maker of Bebe Mascotte), then in 1899 Jules Mettais took over the firm. In 1906 the company was sold to Edmond Daspres.

In 1889 the firm registered the girl with the banner and the words "Le Petite Parisien", and in 1892 LeFosse registered the trademark "Le Parisien". Marks:

J. STEINER   STE C3
BTE S.G.D.G.   J. STEINER
FIRE A 12   B. S.G.D.G.
PARIS

Bourgoin

"A" Series Steiner child: Closed mouth, paperweight eyes, jointed composition body and cardboard pate. No damage, nicely dressed in French styles: 12" – $2,000.00; 16" – $2,600.00; 20" – $3,400.00; 25" – $4,400.00; 28" – $5,000.00.

"A" Series Child: With open mouth, paperweight eyes and on jointed composition body. Nicely dressed in the French style and no damage: 16" – $1,200.00; 20" – $2,300.00; 26" – $3,400.00.

Bourgoin Steiner: With "Bourgoin" incised or in red stamp on head along with rest of the mark. Closed mouth and paperweight eyes. Composition body. No damage in any way and nicely dressed in Frenchy style: 16" – $3,600.00; 20" – $3,900.00; 25" – $4,800.00.

Wire eyed Steiner: Closed mouth with flat glass eyes that open and close by moving wire that comes out the back of the head. Composition body. No damage, chips or breaks and nicely dressed in French styles. Marked: Bourgoin: 16" – $3,800.00; 20" – $4,200.00; 25" – $4,600.00.

C. Series: 16" – $3,800.00; 20" – $4,200.00; 25" – $4,600.00.

A. Series: 16" – $3,800.00; 20" – $4,200.00; 25" – $4,600.00.

"C" Series Steiner: Closed mouth and paperweight eyes and on composition body. No damage and nicely dressed in French style: 16" – $3,500.00; 20" – $3,900.00; 25" – $4,500.00.

Mechanical Steiner: Key wound, kicks, cries, moves head and has two rows of teeth. In working order, not damaged and nicely dressed: 18" – $1,700.00.

Bisque hip Steiner: Motschmann style body with bisque head, shoulders, lower arms and legs and bisque torso section. No damage anywhere and nicely dressed: 18" – $3,600.00.

Early white bisque Steiner: With round face, open mouth with two rows of teeth. Unmarked. On jointed Steiner body. No damage and nicely dressed: 14" – $1,200.00; 18" – $2,600.00.

18" "A" series Steiner with closed mouth, paperweight eyes and on composition body with straight wrists. Original clothes and shoes. Courtesy Turn of Century Antiques. 18" – $2,300.00.

27″ Wire eyed Steiner with closed mouth and original wig and clothes. Wire comes out back of head to operate the eyes. 27″ – $4,800.00.

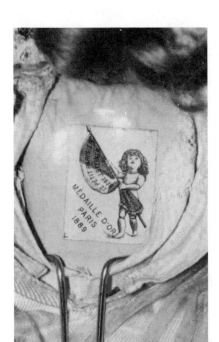

Paper label found on Steiner bodies.

20″ Key wound kicking and crying Steiner with open mouth and two rows of teeth. Body parts are composition and kid. Paperweight eyes. Original clothes. Courtesy Kimport Dolls. 20″ – $1,800.00.

TYNIE BABY
UNICA

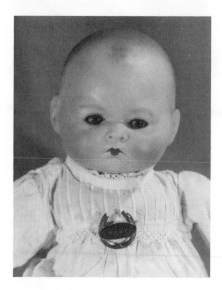

TYNIE BABY. Designed by Bernard Lipfert and made for Horsman Dolls in 1924. Sleep eyes. Clsoed mouth with pouty look and modeling of frown between eyes. Cloth body with composition or celluloid hands. Marks: 1924/E.I.Horsman Inc./Made in/Germany. Some will be incised "Tynie Baby" also. No damage and nicely dressed. Bisque head: 14″ – $650.00; Composition head: 13″-14″ – $245.00.

18″ Painted papier mache. Glass eyes. Open mouth with very dark red lips. Original wig. Marks: Unica/Couraria/Belgium, in a circle with 56 in center. Courtesy Jay Minter. 18″ – $295.00.

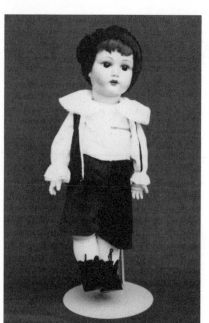

19″ Marked: Unica/Belgium, in a circle with 56 in center. Head is composition with set eyes and open mouth. On jointed composition toddler body. Courtesy Yesterday's Child. 19″ – $325.00.

"Unis,France" was a type of trade association, a type of "seal of approval" for trade goods to consumers from the manufacturers. Often the guide rules of this group of business men, who were supposed to watch the quality of French export items, were overlooked and some rather poor quality dolls escaped them, but there are many very fine quality Unis marked dolls also.

Unis began right after World War I and it is still in effect today. Two doll companies are current members, Poupee Bella and Petit Colin. There are other types of manufacturers in this group and they include makers of toys, sewing machines, tile, pens, etc. Marks:

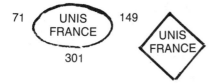

15" Marked: Unis/France, in oval/251/71 149. Open mouth with two upper teeth and sleep eyes with hair lashes. Courtesy Jay Minter. 15" – $800.00.

#60, 70, 71, 301: Bisque head with papier mache or composition jointed body. Sleep or set eyes, open mouth. Not damaged and nicely dressed: 14" – $450.00; 17" – $525.00; 21" – $650.00; 24" – $750.00.

Black or Brown: 14" – $525.00; 17" – $600.00.

Provincial costume doll: Bisque head, painted, set or sleep eyes, open mouth (or closed on smaller dolls). Five-piece body. Original Provincial costume. No damage and in very good condition: 6" – $165.00; 12" – $265.00; 14" – $295.00.

Black or Brown: 6" – $200.00; 12" – $325.00; 14" – $325.00.

On fully jointed body: 12" – $300.00; 14" – $365.00.

24" Sleep eyes, open mouth. Marks: Unis/70, on head and has Jumeau stamp on composition jointed body. Courtesy Margaret Gunnel. 24" – $750.00.

UNIS
UNKNOWN

14½″ Marked: Unis/France/60. Fired-in skin color, open mouth and set eyes. Original costume. Courtesy Kimport Dolls. 14½″ – $450.00.

33″ Marked: P/Made in Germany. Bisque turned shoulder head with kid body. Pin jointed elbows with bisque lower arms. Sleep eyes and open mouth. May be original wig and dress. Courtesy Pat Timmons. 33″ – $1,500.00.

19″ Marked: Germany 12. Bisque head with sleep eyes and open mouth with upper teeth. On jointed composition body. 19″ – $365.00.

15½" Closed mouth with bisque head and shoulder plate in one piece. Paperweight set eyes and kid body with bisque lower arms. Unmarked. Courtesy Kimport Dolls. 15½" – $800.00.

12" Bisque head with set eyes, open mouth with two upper teeth that have a space between. On jointed composition body. Marks: 41.23. Courtesy Jay Minter. 12" – $285.00.

9" Girl with modeled on bonnet, intaglio eyes and open/closed mouth with two painted lower teeth. Marks: 26-12/0. She is on a five-piece crude body. Courtesy Jane Walker. 9" – $425.00.

UNKNOWN

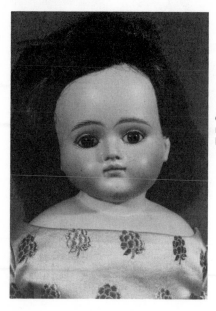

18" German unmarked turned shoulder head on kid body with bisque lower arms. Closed mouth and set glass eyes. Courtesy Kimport Dolls. 18" – $1,000.00.

8" Marked: 1910/Germany. On five-piece papier mache body, open mouth and glass eyes. Has painted-on shoes and socks. Courtesy Kimport Dolls. 8" – $185.00.

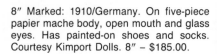

13" With both marked: 1902/910. Five-piece composition body, set glass eyes, open mouth. Boy is original. Courtesy Pat Timmons. 13" – $300.00.

WAGNER & ZETSCHE WAX

Richard Wagner and Richard Zetzsche made dolls, doll's bodies, doll's heads and doll's shoes. They operated in Il-menau,Thur,Germany between 1870's and the 1930's. They used a blue paper label on the shoulder (inside) with the initials W & Z which is in heavy interwoven script, as well as block printed letters. They exported both kid and cloth bodies. The majority of the turned head dolls where the head has been removed to examine the Wagner & Zetzsche label are unmarked. Marked heads have also been found on the W & Z bodies and some of the head makers are: Simon & Halbig, Kestner, and Heinrich Handwerck.

Turned head dolls: Can have solid dome or cut open pate, set, paperweight or sleep eyes, cloth or kid body with bisque lower arms. Eyebrows are flat on the underside. Large sizes may have applied ears. No damage with only minor damage or repair to body and nicely dressed: Closed mouth: 16″ – $750.00; 20″ – $1,100.00; 24″ – $1,500.00.

Open mouth: 20″ – $495.00; 24″ – $750.00; 28″ – $900.00.

28″ Turned shoulder head with applied ears, open mouth, set eyes and is on kid body with bisque lower arms. Courtesy Marcia Piecewicz. 28″ – $1,900.00.

WAX

Poured wax: Cloth body with wax head, arms and legs. Inset glass eyes and hair is embedded into wax. often the eyelashes and eyebrows are also embedded hair into wax. Very nicely dressed or in original clothes, no damge to wax, but wax may be slightly discolored (evenly all over): Not rewaxed: 15″ – $900.00; 18″ – $1,100.00; 21″ – $1,250.00; 24″ – $1,500.00.

Waxed over papier mache or composition: Cloth body with wax over papier mache or composition head and with wax over composition or wood limbs. Only minor scuffs with no chipped out places, nicely dressed:

Pumpkin head: Molded or wigged and glass eyes: 14″ – $200.00; 17″ – $325.00; 21″ – $450.00.

Bonnet molded on: May have mohair or human hair glued over molded hair, glass eyes: 14″ – $395.00; 18″ – $500.00.

Wax with wig: Not modeled as "pumpkin" heads but regular hair styles, open or closed mouth, glass eyes: 17″ – $325.00; 21″ – $385.00; 25″ – $450.00.

Slit-head wax: Human hair embedded into slit down center of head. Glass eyes: 17″ – $425.00; 21″ – $500.00.

WAX

25½" Early molded hair wax with snood. Glass inset eyes and on sawdust filled cloth body.. Wax over wood arms and legs. Ca. 1850. Courtesy Kimport Dolls. 25½" – $1,300.00.

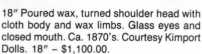

18" Poured wax, turned shoulder head with cloth body and wax limbs. Glass eyes and closed mouth. Ca. 1870's. Courtesy Kimport Dolls. 18" – $1,100.00.

14" "Pompadour" wax over papier mache with glass eyes and original wig over molded hair. Cloth body with wax lower limbs. Ca. 1885. Courtesy Kimport Dolls. 14" – $265.00.

21½" "Pumpkin wax" of the 1880's. Shoulder head on cloth body with wax lower limbs. Eyes are painted to look like glass. Courtesy Kimport Dolls. 21½" – $450.00.

22" German wax over papier mache of 1885. Inset glass eyes, closed mouth. Original wig is embedded along the part line only. Courtesy Kimport Dolls. 22" – $495.00.

42" Wax over composition shoulder head, glass eyes and closed mouth. Kid body with legs of cloth. Marked inside of shoulder: H. Courtesy Bonnie Stewart. 42" – $1,600.00.

WELLINGS, NORAH

Norah Wellings' designs were made for her at the Victoria Toy Works in Wellington, Shropshire, England. These dolls were made from 1926 into the 1960's. The dolls are felt, velour and velvet as well as other fabrics. They will have a tag on the foot: Made in England by Norah Wellings. **Child:** All fabric with stitch jointed hips and shoulders and have a molded fabric face with oil painted fetures. Some faces are of papier mache with a stockinet covering. All original felt and cloth clothes, clean condition: Painted eyes: 14″ – $200.00; 17″ – $350.00; 21″ – $475.00.

Glass eyes: 14″ – $285.00; 17″ – $475.00; 21″ – $595.00.

Mounties, Black Islanders, Scots and other characters: These are most commonly found. Must be in same condition as children: 8″ – $45.00; 11″ – $70.00; 14″ – $95.00; 17″ – $165.00.

Babies: Same description as "child" and same condition: 14″ – $285.00; 17″ – $475.00; 21″ – $595.00.

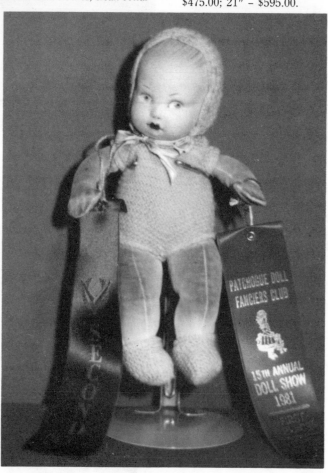

10″ Baby that is all velvet, painted features and tag: Made in England/by/Norah Wellings. Courtesy Eileen Flores. 10″ – $200.00.

WELLINGS, NORAH

15″ All velvet with painted features, sewn on wig and original clothes. Tag: Made in England/by/Norah Wellings. Courtesy Johnston Collection. 15″ – $265.00.

17″ "Tak-Uki". All velvet cloth with rooted skull cap wig. Inset eyes, open style mouth with painted teeth. Tag: Made in England/by/Norah Wellings. Courtesy Allin Collection. 17″ – $185.00.

8″ "Miss Smith" (on paper tag). All cloth with sewn on mohair wig. Painted features. All original. 8″ – $45.00.

MODERN DOLL SECTION

ADVERTISING DOLLS

Alka Seltzer "Speedy": 7½" – $8.00.
Betty Crocker doll: 13". All cloth with brown suede hair and yarn ponytails. Very large eyes and wears red-white check dress and white apron with red applique – $16.00.
Borden's "Elsie cow": 15". Plush and vinyl. Early 1950's has vinyl face and high heel boot hoofs: – $18.00; Late 1950's with aqua plush body: – $16.00; 1970's with yellow felt hooves and brown plush body: – $12.00.
Buster Brown Mannikins: 32" size 2 garments – $95.00; Baby size 12 months – $75.00; 25" Girl – $85.00.
Capt. Crunch: 15½" Made by Quaker Oats 1978 – $6.00.
Campbell Kids: 10" vinyl Bicentennial dolls and dressed in Colonial style – $45.00 pair.
Chiquita Banana Doll: All printed cloth 16" – $8.00.
Diaparine Baby: 6" – $4.00.
Fab Doll: 8" All hard plastic – $20.00; 9" All hard plastic – $25.00.
Faultless Starch: Printed cloth to be cut and sewn. "Miss Phoebe Primm" and "Miss Lilly White" – $45.00 each.
Green Giant: All cloth 6" – $9.00; "Country Girl", 18", 1957 – $65.00; 1956 – $65.00; 6" "Sprout" – $2.00; 9" "Jolly Green Giant" – $8.00; 12" "Sprout" – $5.00.
"Itylyti". 16" All cloth made for Brunswick – $12.00.
Jack Frost: All cloth dolls, 14" – $4.00; 16" – $6.00.
Keebler Elf-Keebler Cookie Co. 6½" – $6.00; 16" – $9.00. All fleece/felt – $12.00.
Lucky Charms: All cloth and felt – $14.00.
Luvs Diaper Dolls: 13½" – $6.00; 17" – $9.00.
Libby Cloth doll: 14" – $12.00.
McDonald, Ronald: 13½" – $5.00; 17" – $7.00; Girl: 11" – $5.00.
Mermaid: 24" – $70.00.
Nestle Chocolate "Hans". 13" – $22.00.
Roni Mac for American Beauty. 11" Cut and sew cloth doll. Head shaped like a cylinder – $35.00.

Shoney dolls: 14" cloth boy – $6.00; 10" Dog – $5.00; 14" Dolly" – $6.00. Shoney boy: 8" – $4.00; 9" – $7.00; 10" – $8.00; 11" – $10.00.
Snap, Crackle & Pop by Kelloggs: All vinyl, jointed neck only. Set of 3 – $8.00.

25" Composition shoulder head with painted features and molded hair under wig. Very short composition arms with rest of doll stuffed cloth. Tin disc jointed hips. Original dress with tag: Poll Parrot Shoes. Courtesy Bonnie Stewart. 25" – $125.00.

"Buster Brown" manikins boy and girl. Used to display Buster Brown clothes. Marks: Buster Brown. Size 2 garments. Old King Cole, Inc. Courtesy Jeannie Mauldin. 32" – $95.00.

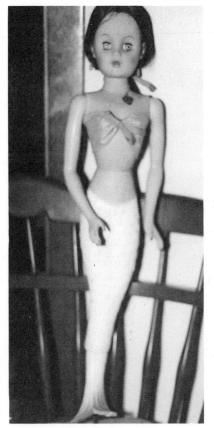

20" "Mermaid" for Chicken of the Sea Tuna. Marked Mermaid Doll Co. 1965. White tail toned in blue. Cloth halter added. Gold heart necklace and pearl earrings. Wire in bottom of tail pulls out to about 24" long, and use is unknown. Courtesy Jayn Allen. 20" – $70.00.

17" Tall and 14" long early 1950's "Elsie". Brown plush, vinyl face and feet and milk sack. Marks: BiJOU-TOY. Courtesy Jeannie Mauldin. 17" – $22.00.

ADVERTISING DOLLS

15" Buster Brown and 9" Tige. Both are stuffed with printed on details. On his back pocket is: 1974 Buster Brown. Courtesy Jeannie Mauldin. $47.00

"Snap, Crackle & Pop" by Kelloggs. All vinyl of the squeeze toy type. First issued in 1975. Courtesy Jeannie Mauldin. $8.00.

15″ "Lucky Charms". All felt. Plastic eyes. Tag: Animal Fair-General Mills. 1979. 15″ "Capt. Crunch". All felt, plastic eyes. Tag: The Quaker Oats Co., Animal Fair, copyright. 1978. Courtesy Jeannie Mauldin. $14.00.

16″ 1979 ad doll for Welch Grape Juice. All stuffed with vinyl mask face, painted features and rooted hair and beard. Tag: Soft and Safe. Animal Fair. Please Hug Me. 1979. Has "W" on front of belt. Courtesy Jeannie Mauldin. $9.00.

11″ Ad doll for McDonalds. Plastic and vinyl with rooted hair and painted features and has "golden Archs" on shirt front. Doll unmarked. Courtesy Jeannie Mauldin.

ADVERTISING DOLLS

14″ "Mother Nature" for Chiffon margarine. All one-piece stuffed cloth, brown yarn hair, painted features. Yellow ribbon belt marked: Chiffon's Mother Nature. Tag: Animal Fair. Mother Nature, Chiffon. 1983. Courtesy Jeannie Mauldin. $7.00.

11″ Little Debbie Snack Cakes doll. Plastic and vinyl, painted features with painted teeth. Name on pinafore. All original. Marks: Horsman Doll Inc. 1978, on head. Horsman Doll, on back. Tag: 1984 McKee Baking Co., on dress. Courtesy Jeannie Mauldin. $7.00.

12″ "Snow White" advertising doll for Final Touch fabric softner. Cloth body and limbs, vinyl head with painted features. Tag on dress: Applause Div. of Wallace Berry & Co. Woodland Hills, Calif. Walt Disney Productions. 1985. Courtesy Jeannie Mauldin. $12.00.

MADAME ALEXANDER-ALEXANDER-KINS

Alexander-kins: All hard plastic, sleep eyes, jointed at shoulders, neck and hips. Can be 7½" or 8".
Marks: "ALEX.", on backs and full name "ALEXANDER" after 1977.
TAGS: "Alexander-kins", "Madame Alexander, etc.", specific name of doll, or "WENDY-KINS'.

1953 - straight leg, non-walker. All solid, heavy hard plastic.

1954 - straight leg, non walker & straight leg walker.

1955 - straight leg walker.

1956-1965 - bend knee walker.

1973 to date - straight leg non-walker, light weight.

1973-1975 - marked: "Alex".

1976 to date - marked: "Alexander"

1978 - face change to smaller painted mouth.

1981 to date - very pale color.

Prices For Mint, Tagged Dolls With Original Box.

Alexander-kin/Wendy-kins: Short dresses, no pinafores - $185.00 up. Dirty, hair messy, no shoes - $50.00.

Pinafore/dresses with hats - $225.00 up. Dirty, hair messy, no tag or shoes - $60.00.

Brides: 1953-54 - $525.00; 1955 - $425.00; 1970's - $65.00. Dirty & played with - $85.00-125.00.

Groom - $500.00. Dirty - $125.00.

Ballgowns - $500.00 up. Fading, tag gone, hats or hair flowers gone - $150.00.

Ballerinas: 1950's - $375.00; 1960's - $250.00. Dirty - $60.00-85.00.

Guardian Angel - $1,600.00. Fading, halo or harp missing - $300.00.

Nurse: In white - $900.00; Dirty - $100.00. In Blue/white - $900.00; Dirty, baby missing - $100.00.

Special long gowns: Melanie - $1,400.00; Dirty - $200.00. Aunt Pitty Pat - $1,900.00; Dirty - $225.00. Aunt Agatha - $1,200.00; Dirty - $175.00. Cousin Grace - $1,400.00; Dirty - $200.00.

Quiz-kin: Has buttons in back to move head - $650.00; Played with & not mint - $175.00.

Story Princess - $1,400.00; Soiled, tiara missing - $200.00.
International - discontinued: Africa - $575.00; Soiled - $250.00.

Amish boy or girl - $550.00; Soiled - $225.00.

Argentine boy - $500.00; Soiled - $200.00.

Boliva - $600.00; Soiled - $285.00.

Cowboy or girl - $650.00; Soiled - $295.00.

Ecuador - $500.00; Soiled - $200.00.

English Guard - $500.00; Soiled - $200.00.

Eskimo - $650.00; Soiled - $295.00.

Hawaii - $525.00; Soiled - $215.00.

Greek boy - $500.00; Soiled - $200.00.

Indian boy or girl - $500.00; Soiled - $200.00.

Korea - $475.00; Soiled - $175.00.

Morocco - $500.00; Soiled - $200.00.

Miss U.S.A. - $325.00; Soiled - $100.00.

Peruvian boy - $525.00; Soiled - $215.00.

Spanish boy - $465.00; Soiled - $165.00.

Vietnam - $525.00; Soiled - $215.00.

Bend Knee Internationals - $65.00 each.

Straight Leg: S.A.

Storybook Dolls with Bend Knees - $75.00 each.

Straight Leg: S.A.

MADAME ALEXANDER-ALEXANDER-KINS

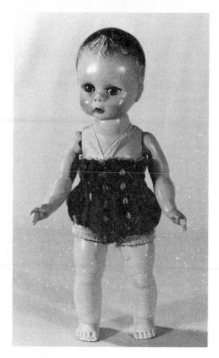

1953-1954 Quiz-kin. Came with molded hair and wig over molded hair. Buttons in back make head move. Courtesy Jay Minter. $300.00

Cowgirl of 1967. Has bend knees. Courtesy Jay Minter. $650.00.

Bend knee walker of 1956 "Bridesmaid". Hat is replaced. Courtesy Jay Minter. $425.00.

MADAME ALEXANDER-ALEXANDER-KINS
MADAME ALEXANDER-BABIES

8" Alexander-kin in school style dress. Bend knee walker, hat added. Courtesy Jay Minter. $175.00.

Alexander-kin Nurse that is a 1956 bend knee walker. Right is a Vogue Ginny Nurse. Courtesy Jay Minter. $550.00. Ginny: $200.00.

MADAME ALEXANDER-BABIES

Prices are for mint dolls.

Baby McGuffey, composition. 20" – $225.00; Soiled – $75.00.

Bonnie, vinyl. 19" – $175.00; Soiled – $90.00.

Cookie, composition. 19" – $250.00; Soiled – $85.00.

Genius, vinyl, flirty eyes. 21" – $250.00; Soiled – $85.00.

Genius, Little. 8" – $195.00; Soiled – $95.00.

Happy, vinyl. 20" – $250.00; Soiled – $85.00.

Honeybun, vinyl. 23" – $165.00; Soiled – $75.00.

Kathy, vinyl. 19" – $185.00. 26" – $225.00; Soiled – $85.00-95.00.

Kitten, Littlest, vinyl. 8" – $200.00; Soiled – $65.00.

Mary Mine. 14" – $150.00; Soiled – $45.00.

Pinky, compositon. 23" – $150.00; Soiled – $45.00.

Precious, composition. 12" – $150.00; Soiled – $45.00.

Princess Alexandria. 24" – $175.00; Soiled – $80.00.

Pussy Cat. Black. 14" – $250.00; Soiled – $85.00.

Rusty, vinyl. 20" – $365.00; Soiled – $100.00.

Slumbermate, composition. 21" – $400.00; Soiled – $125.00.

Sunbeam, vinyl. 16" – $200.00; Soiled – $65.00.

Sweet Tears. 9" – $125.00 with layette – $150.00 up; Soiled – $25.00-45.00.

Victoria. 20" – $195.00; Soiled – $90.00.

MADAME ALEXANDER-BABIES

23" Kathy of 1959. All original. Came in 11", 15", 17", 19" and 26" also. Courtesy Jay Minter. 23" – $195.00.

Little Genuis of 1950's. Vinyl with hard plastic head. Courtesy Jay Minter. $195.00.

14" Sweet Tears (in picture) with layette. Discontinued in 1983. Courtesy Jay Minter. $150.00 up.

20″ "Pussy Cat", 16″ "Pussy Cat" and 20″ "Mommie's Pet". The Pussy Cats are in discontinued clothes and their doll has been discontinued. Courtesy Turn of Century Antiques. 20″ – $95.00; 16″ – $75.00.

MADAME ALEXANDER-CISSETTE

First prices are for mint dolls. Second prices are for soiled, dirty or faded clothes, tags missing or hair messy. High heel doll, all hard plastic. Made from 1957 to 1963 as "Cissette", but used as other dolls later. Clothes are tagged: "Cissette", 10″-11″.
In street dresses – $200.00-85.00.
In Ballgowns – $350.00-125.00.
Ballerina – $350.00-100.00.
Gibson Girl – $1,500.00-300.00.
Jacqueline – $550.00-150.00.
Margot – $495.00-125.00.
Portrettes:
Agatha, 1968 – $575.00-165.00.
Godey, 1968-1970 - $500.00-125.00.

Jenny Lind, 1969-1970 – $650.00-195.00.
Melinda in turquoise, 1968 – $525.00-125.00.
Melinda in pink lace, 1969 – $585.00-165.00.
Melanie, 1970 – $485.00-115.00.
Queen – $475.00-100.00.
Renoir in navy, 1968 – $475.00-115.00.
Renoir in aqua, 1970 – $475.00-115.00.
Scarlett, 1968-1973 – $485.00-100.00.
Southern Belle, 1968-1973 – $550.00-165.00.
Sleeping Beauty – $475.00-135.00.
Wigged, in case – $700.00-350.00.

MADAME ALEXANDER-CISSETTE

"Cissette" in ballgown. 1957 to 1963 in various ones. Courtesy Jay Minter. $350.00.

"Wigged Cissette" in box with extra wigs and clothes. Courtesy Jay Minter. $700.00.

"Margot" using the "Cissette" doll. Has blue eyes made-up as did the "Jacqueline". This is a "Jacqueline" style hairdo. Courtesy Jay Minter. $495.00.

10″ "Godey Lady" Portrette and 8″ "Amish Girl". Both discontinued. Courtesy Turn of Century Antiques. 10″ – $395.00; 8″ – $300.00.

10″-11″ "Cissette Ballerina" 1957-1959. Courtesy Jay Minter. $250.00.

"Cissette" in one of her many street dresses. Courtesy Jay Minter $175.00.

MADAME ALEXANDER-CISSY
MADAME ALEXANDER-CLOTH DOLLS

First prices are for mint dolls. Second prices for played with, soiled, messed up dolls. High heel feet, vinyl arms jointed at elbows. 1955-1959. Clothes tag, "Cissy". 21" tall.
Ballgown: - $350.00-165.00.
Bride: - $400.00-125.00.

Flora McFlimsey, Miss (vinyl head) 15" - $450.00-185.00.
Queen - $550.00-150.00.
Portrait (Godey, etc.) - $550.00-200.00.
Scarlett - $700.00-225.00.
Street Dressed - $225.00-95.00.

"Cissy-Queen" in white brocade and deep navy blue cape with red lining. Cape has outline of "jewels" and gold braid on navy velvet. Courtesy Turn of Century Antiques. $550.00

"Cissy" in street dress and trunk with original clothes. Courtesy Turn of Century Antiques. $700.00.

MADAME ALEXANDER-CLOTH DOLLS

Cloth Dolls. First prices are for mint dolls. Second prices for poor condition, dirty or played with dolls or untagged. The Alexander Doll Company made cloth and plush dolls and animals and also oil cloth baby animal toys in the 1930's, 1940's and early 1950's. In the 1960's there were a few, such as "Funny", "Muffin" and "Good or Bad Little Girl".

Animals - $300.00 up-100.00.
Dogs - $300.00-100.00.
Alice In Wonderland - $450.00-125.00.
Clarabelle Clown - $19" - $225.00-95.00.
David Copperfield - $500.00-150.00.
Eva Lovelace - $400.00-125.00.
Funny - $95.00-35.00.

MADAME ALEXANDER-CLOTH DOLLS

Good or Bad Little Girl – $150.00-
65.00.
Little Shaver – 7″ – $200.00-85.00; 10″
– $275.00-95.00; 16″ – $350.00-125.00.
Little Women – $450.00-150.00.
Muffin – $175.00-65.00.

So-Lite baby or toddler – $300.00-95.00.
Susie Q or Bobby Q 16″ – $600.00-
150.00.
Tiny Tim – $450.00-125.00.
Teeny Twinkle – $465.00-200.00.

"Teeny Twinkle" with oil cloth body, mask
face with FLIRTY, movable celluloid disc
eyes. Tag: "Teeny Twinkle" by Madame
Alexander. Courtesy Nancy Cellitti. $465.00.

"Tiny Tim" and so tagged. Cloth with face
mask and painted features. Courtesy Nancy Cellitti. $450.00.

MADAME ALEXANDER-CLOTH DOLLS
MADAME ALEXANDER-COMPOSITION DOLLS

7" and 10" "Little Shaver". Tagged: Little Shaver. Courtesy Jay Minter. 7" # $200.00; 10" # $275.00.

16" "Susie Q". 1940. All cloth and felt. Courtesy Jay Minter. $600.00.

MADAME ALEXANDER-COMPOSITION DOLLS

Composition Dolls 1st prices are for mint dolls. 2nd prices for cracked, crazed, dirty or soiled clothes, or tags gone.
Alice In Wonderland 9" – $225.00-75.00; 14" – $350.00-90.00; 20" – $575.00-100.00.
Babies (Genius, McGuffey, etc.). 11" – $165.00-65.00; 22" – $250.00-85.00.
Baby Jane 16" – $700.00-200.00.
Brides-Bridesmaids 7" – $185.00-80.00; 9" – $225.00-80.00; 15" – $285.00-95.00; 21" – $475.00-100.00.
Dionne Quints 8" – $185.00-80.00; Set of five. $1,200.00.

11" – $275.00-95.00; Set $1,800.00.

14" – $350.00-100.00; Set $2,000.00.

16" – $450.00-125.00; Set $2,400.00.

19" – $475.00-150.00; Set $3,000.00.
Dr. Defoe 14"-15" – $650.00-125.00.
Flora McFlimsey (marked Princess Elizabeth). Freckles. 15" – $425.00-100.00; 22" – $525.00-150.00.
Internationals/Storybook 7" – $185.00-65.00; 11" – $225.00-80.00.
Jane Withers 13" with closed mouth – $725.00-150.00; 17" – $750.00-150.00; 21" – $900.00-175.00.

MADAME ALEXANDER-COMPOSITION DOLLS

Jeannie Walker 13″ – $325.00-125.00; 18″ – $500.00-145.00.

Karen Ballerina (and other composition ballerinas): 15″ – $350.00-95.00.

Kate Greenaway (Marked Princess Elizabeth) 14″ – $375.00-120.00; 18″ – $500.00-165.00.

Little Colonel 9″ – $225.00-80.00; 13″ (Closed mouth) – $375.00-120.00; 23″ – $675.00-185.00.

Margaret O'Brien 15″ – $500.00-125.00; 18″ – $600.00-150.00; 21″ – $950.00-200.00.

Marionettes Tony Sarg: 12″ – $275.00-85.00; Disney: 12″ – $300.00-95.00.

McGuffey Ana (Marked Princess Elizabeth) 13″ – $350.00-100.00; 20″ – $500.00-165.00.

Portrait Dolls. 1939-1941, 1946: 21″ – $1,200.00-200.00.

Princess Elizabeth 13″ – (Closed mouth) $300.00-95.00; 18″ – $450.00-100.00; 24″ – $500.00-125.00.

Scarlett 9″ – $300.00-95.00; 14″ – $450.00-125.00; 18″ – $600.00-175.00; 21″ – $800.00-195.00.

Sonja Henie 17″ – $500.00-100.00; 20″ – $550.00-100.00; Jointed waist: 14″ – $375.00-85.00.

Three Pigs 11″ – $425.00-100.00; Set of three: $1,400.00.

Special Girl 22″-23″ – $450.00-125.00.

Wendy Ann 11″ – $350.00-85.00; 15″ – $350.00-95.00; 18″ – $400.00-100.00.

21″ 1945-46 Portrait ''Antoinette''. All composition and all original. Tag: Madame Alexander. New York U.S.A. Courtesy Turn of Century Antiques. $1,200.00 up.

21″ Portrait ''Carmen''. All composition and all original. Tag: Madame Alexander. New York. U.S.A. Courtesy Turn of Century Antiques. $1,200.00 up.

MADAME ALEXANDER-COMPOSITION DOLLS

21″ ''Flavia'' from the movie ''Prisoner of Zenda''. All composition and original. Tag: Madame Alexander. New York, U.S.A. Courtesy Turn of Century Antiques. $1,200.00 up.

MADAME ALEXANDER-COMPOSITION DOLLS

21″ Portrait of 1945-46. "Melanie". All composition and all original. Tag: Madame Alexander, New York, U.S.A. Courtesy Turn of Century Antiques. $1,200.00 up.

21″ Portrait "Ballerina from a Degas painting". All composition and original. 1945-46. Tag: Madame Alexander. New York, U.S.A. Courtesy Turn of Century Antiques. $1,200.00 up.

11″ "MuGuffey Ana". Has closed mouth. All original and tagged. Courtesy Shirley Bertrand. $450.00.

MADAME ALEXANDER-HARD PLASTIC

Hard Plastics 1st prices are for mint dolls. 2nd for soiled, dirty, played with or untagged dolls.

Alice In Wonderland 14″ – $350.00-100.00; 17″ – $425.00-125.00; 23″ – $600.00-200.00.

Annabelle 15″ – $400.00-100.00; 18″ – $550.00-125.00; 23″ – $650.00-200.00.

Babs 20″ – $400.00-125.00. **Babs Skater** 18″ – $495.00-165.00; 21″ – $550.00-195.00.

Binnie Walker 15″ – $285.00-95.00; 25″ – $400.00-125.00.

Ballerina 14″ – $275.00-100.00.

Cinderella 14″ – $600.00-200.00; 18″ – $700.00-250.00.

Cynthia (Black doll): 15″ – $625.00-200.00; 18″ – $675.00-200.00; 23″ – $750.00-250.00.

Elise 16½″ street dress – $300.00-95.00; **Ballgown** – $375.00-100.00; **Bride** – $300.00-95.00.

Fairy Queen 14½″ – $500.00-100.00; 18″ – $500.00-100.00.

Glamour Girls 18″ – $700.00-150.00.

Godey Lady 14″ – $700.00-150.00; **Bride** $700.00-150.00; **Man/Groom** $750.00-150.00.

Kathy 15″ – $300.00-95.00; 18″ – $350.00-95.00.

Kelly 12″ – $600.00-100.00; 16″ – $275.00-95.00.

Lady Churchill 18″ – $800.00-125.00.

Lissy 12″ Street dress – $275.00-95.00; **Bride** $275.00-95.00; **Ballgown** $300.00-100.00.

Lissy 12″ **Ballerina** $300.00-100.00; **Bridesmaid** $275.00-95.00.

Lissy Classics, such as McGuffey Ana, Cinderella, etc. – $1,600.00-200.00.

Little Women 14″ – $300.00 each-95.00; 14″ set of five – $1,600.00.

Little Women 12″ (Lissy) – $350.00 each-$95.00; **Laurie** – $375.00.

Little Women 8″ straight leg walker – $225.00 each-70.00.

Maggie 15″ – $300.00-95.00; 17″ – $350.00-95.00; 23″ – $400.00-100.00.

Maggie Mixup 8″ – $450.00-100.00; 16½″ – $375.00-100.00; 8″ **Angel** – $1,900.00-200.00.

14″ "Babs Skater" 1949-1950. Outfit came in blue, yellow, pink and all have gold trim. $395.00.

17″ "Nina Ballerina" outfit is red with gold trim. 1953. $350.00.

MADAME ALEXANDER-HARD PLASTIC

Margaret O'Brien 14½" – $600.00-125.00; 18" – $700.00-125.00; 22" – $1,000.00-200.00.

Margaret Rose, Princess: 14" – $425.00-100.00; 18" – $450.00-100.00.

Mary Martin 14" Sailor suit – $650.00-150.00; 17" – $600.00-150.00.

Nina Ballerina – 14" – $275.00-100.00; 17" – $350.00-125.00.

Peter Pan 15" – $500.00-200.00.

Polly Pigtails 14" – $295.00-95.00; 17" – $325.00-125.00.

Prince Charming 14" – $700.00-200.00; 18" – $850.00-200.00; 21" – $900.00-225.00.

Prince Phillip 17" – $500.00-150.00; 21" – $600.00-150.00.

Queen 18" – $600.00-150.00.

Shari Lewis 14" – $350.00-100.00; 21" – $475.00-125.00.

Sleeping Beauty 16¼" – $485.00-100.00; 21" – $500.00-150.00.

Story Princess 15" – $450.00-125.00.

Violet, Sweet 18" – $450.00-100.00.

Wendy (Peter Pan): 14" – $450.00-95.00.

Wendy Ann 14½" – $275.00-85.00; 17" – $300.00-85.00; 22" – $350.00-95.00.

Winnie Walker 15" – $250.00-95.00; 18" – $275.00-95.00; 23" – $300.00-125.00.

14" 1950 "Prince Charming" and "Cinderella". Courtesy Mary Williams. $600.00 each.

MADAME ALEXANDER-HARD PLASTIC

20" "Annabelle". All hard plastic and original. 17" "Maggie Mixup". Plastic and vinyl and all original. Courtesy Turn of Century Antiques. 20" – $550.00; 17" – $300.00.

14" "McGuffey Ana". All hard plastic. All original except shoes. 13" "McGuffey Ana". All composition and all original. Courtesy Turn of Century Antiques. 14" – $185.00; 13" – $245.00.

12" Lissy in street dress. All original. Jointed elbows and knees. Courtesy Jay Minter. $275.00.

MADAME ALEXANDER
PLASTIC AND VINYL DOLLS

1st Prices are for mint dolls. 2nd for soiled, dirty, played with or untagged dolls.

Barbara Jane 29″ - $350.00-125.00.

Caroline 15″ - $385.00-150.00; In riding habit - $450.00-150.00.

Elise 17″ Discontinued bride or bridesmaid - $300.00-125.00.

First Ladies First set of six dolls: $1,700.00; Second set of six dolls: $1,400.00; Third set of six dolls: $900.00.

"Fischer Quints". Hard plastic head, vinyl body: Set of five: $450.00-100.00.

Gidget 14″ - $600.00-175.00.

Granny, Little 14″ - $325.00-125.00.

Jacqueline 21″ in ballgown: $900.00-300.00; street dress - $900.00-250.00; riding habit - $900.00-300.00; 10″ - $550.00-150.00.

Janie 12″ - $300.00-100.00.

Joanie 36″ - $400.00-100.00; Nurse - $475.00-185.00.

Jenny Lind and cat: 14″ - $550.00-200.00.

Katie (Black): 12″ - $350.00-125.00.

Katie (FAO Swartz): 12″ - $1,400.00-250.00.

Leslie (Black) 17″ Ballgown - $450.00-185.00; Ballerina - $325.00-100.00; Bride - $325.00-125.00; Street dress - $325.00-185.00.

Madame Doll 14″ - $475.00-200.00.

Madelaine 18″. Jointed knees, elbows and wrists - $300.00-100.00.

Madelaine 16½″ Rigid vinyl - $325.00-125.00.

Marlo Thomas 17″ - $600″ - $200.00.

Marybel 16″ - $225.00-95.00; in case: $285.00.

Mary Ellen 31″ - $425.00-195.00.

Melinda 14″ - $385.00-100.00; 16″ - $385.00-125.00; 22″ - $400.00-200.00.

Michael with bear: (Peter Pan set) 11″ - $425.00-175.00.

Mimi 30″ - $500.00-200.00.

Peter Pan 15″ - $395.00-165.00.

Polly 17″ - $350.00-125.00.

Rozy 12″ - $400.00-200.00.

Smarty 12″ - $325.00-100.00.

Sound of Music Liesl - 10″ - $275.00-100.00; 14″ - $245.00-100.00.

Louisa - 10″ - $325.00-125.00; 14″ - $295.00-125.00.

Maria - 12″ - $295.00-100.00; 17″ - $345.00-175.00.

Brigitta - 10″ - $225.00-100.00; 14″ - $245.00-100.00.

Marta - 8″ - $195.00 - $95.00; 11″ - $185.00 - $95.00.

Gretl - 8″ - $195.00-95.00; 11″ - $185.00-95.00.

Friedrich - 8″ - $195.00; 11″ - $245.00-100.00.

Small set - $1,700.00; Large set - $1,800.00.

Timmie Toddler 23″ - $225.00-95.00; 30″ - $300.00-125.00.

Tommy (FOA Swartz) - $1,400.00; 250.00.

Wendy of Peter Pan - 14″ - $375.00-100.00.

22″ "Melinda" 1963. Excellent quality vinyl and modeling. Courtesy Jay Minter. $400.00.

MADAME ALEXANDER
PLASTIC AND VINYL DOLLS

15″ "Caroline" All heavy vinyl. 1961. Courtesy Jay Minter. $385.00.

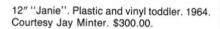

12″ "Janie". Plastic and vinyl toddler. 1964. Courtesy Jay Minter. $300.00.

11″ "Michael with bear" from the Peter Pan set. Courtesy Jay Minter. $425.00.

18" Elise Bride and Bridesmaid in pink. Bride discontinued. Plastic and vinyl. Courtesy Turn of Century Antiques. $150.00 each.

17" "Marlo Thomas" 1967. From T.V. show "That Girl". Courtesy Jay Minter. $600.00.

MADAME ALEXANDER-PORTRAITS

Prices are for mint dolls. The 21" **Portraits** are many and varied. All have the "Jacqueline" face and all will be marked 1961 on the heads as the same molds are being used as they were when "Jacqueline" was first introduced in 1961. 21" – $425.00 up depending upon individual doll.
Coco 1966. 21" Portraits – $2,200.00; street dresses – $2,200.00; Ballgowns (other than portrait series) – $2,200.00.

21" "Coco Scarlett" 1966. The gown is white with red flowers and sash. Courtesy Mary Williams. $2,200.00.

MADAME ALEXANDER-PORTRAITS

21" "Scarlett" in green velvet. "Agatha" in lavender purple and "Melanie" in pink and white.
Courtesy Turn of Century Antiques. $425.00 up.

1978 "Scarlett" in floral print. Courtesy Mary
Willliams. $375.00.

AMERICAN CHARACTER DOLL COMPANY

1st prices are for mint dolls. 2nd for dirty, soiled, redressed or poor condition. The American Character dolls are very collectible. All are above average in quality of materials and clothes. Dolls marked: American Doll and Toy Co. are also American Character dolls, as this name was used from 1959 to 1968 when the entire firm went out of business. Early dolls will be marked: Petite.

Annie Oakley – 17" – $125.00-50.00.

Betsy McCall 8" – $75.00-45.00; 14" – $125.00-65.00; 36" – $250.00-100.00.

Butterball 19" – $125.00-45.00.

Cartwright, Ben, Joe or Hoss 8" – $60.00-20.00.

Chuckles 23" – $150.00-65.00; Baby – 18" – $85.00-35.00.

Composition babies/cloth bodies: marked A.C. – 14" – $55.00-20.00; 22" – $75.00-30.00. Marked: Petite: 14" – $65.00-20.00; 22" – $85.00-30.00.

Cricket 9" – $12.00-4.00.

Hedda-Get-Betta 21" – $65.00-20.00.

Miss Echo, Little: 30" – $125.00-80.00.

Petite marked girls 14" – $120.00-75.00; 20" – $150.00-85.00. Marked A.C.: 14" – $85.00-35.00; 20" – $100.00-45.00.

Popi 12" – $16.00-4.00.

Puggy, frown face marked Petite: 13" – $350.00-125.00.

Ricky Jr. 13" – $55.00-22.00; 20" – $85.00-38.00.

Sally, composition 14" – $125.00-80.00; 18" – $165.00-80.00.

Sally Says plastic/vinyl: 19" – $85.00-35.00.

Sweet Sue/Toni hard plastic: 15" – $85.00-35.00; 18" – $125.00-50.00; 22" – $150.00-50.00; 30" – $295.00-100.00.

Vinyl: 10½" – $50.00-22.00; 17" – $85.00-40.00; 21" – $135.00-60.00; 30" – $295.00-100.00.

Groom: 20" – $150.00-75.00.

Tiny Tears. Hard plastic/vinyl. 8½" – $45.00-15.00; 13" – $75.00-45.00; 17" – $125.00-65.00.

All vinyl: 8" – $22.50-6.00; 12" – $45.00-20.00; 16" – $65.00-30.00.

Toodles: Baby: 14" – $55.00-20.00.

Tiny: 10½" – $75.00-18.00.

Toddler with "follow me eyes": 22" – $95.00-35.00; 28" – $150.00-75.00.

Child with "follow me eyes": 22" – $100.00-35.00; 28" – $165.00-75.00.

Black: 22" – $200.00-95.00.

Toodle-loo 18" – $95.00-35.00.

Tressy 12½" – $18.00-6.00.

Whimette: 7½" – $14.00-4.00.

Whimsey 19" – $95.00-40.00.

22" All composition girl with open mouth, sleep eyes and wig. Marked: Petite. Courtesy Jeannie Mauldin. $185.00.

AMERICAN CHARACTER DOLL COMPANY

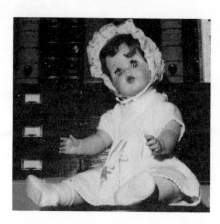

23" "Toodles" with "follow me eyes" and called "Peek-a-Boo Toddles". 1958. Courtesy Phyllis Teague. $95.00.

18" "Sweet Sue" Bride. All hard plastic. all original. Courtesy June Schultz. $125.00.

20" "Sweet Sue" by American Character on left and extreme right. Both all hard plastic and original. Center two dolls are Effanbee's "Anne Shirley/Little Lady" (marked) with one on left having yarn wig and one on right human hair. Both are all composition and original. Courtesy Turn of Century Antiques. Sweet Sue – $85.00; Anne Shirley – $195.00.

AMERICAN CHARACTER DOLL COMPANY
ARRANBEE DOLL COMPANY

19"-20" "Miss Take", on banner and "Betty The Beauty" on tag. Red bathing suit and green sun glasses. Whimmsie of 1960-1961. Courtesy Jeannie Mauldin. $95.00.

10½" "Sweet Sue/Toni". All vinyl with rooted hair. High heel feet. Courtesy Jay Minter. $35.00.

ARRANBEE DOLL COMPANY

First prices are for mint dolls. Second for crazed, dirty, soiled or dolls in poor condition. The Arranbee Doll Company was started in 1922 and purchased by the Vogue Doll Company in 1959. The molds were still used with the name Arranbee (R & B) until 1961. Arranbee had the Armand Marseille firm of Germany make bisque head babies for them in the 1920's, and called them "My Dream Baby" using the mold numbers 341 and 351. (See bisque section under "Armand Marseille for prices).

Babies Composition/cloth bodies: 16" – $45.00-20.00; 22" – $75.00-35.00.
Bottle Tot: Has celluloid bottle molded to celluloid hand: 18" – $125.00-45.00.
Debu-teen: Composition girl wtih cloth body: 14" – $125.00-45.00; 18" – $165.00-50.00.
Dream Baby: Composition – 14" – $95.00-40.00; Vinyl/cloth: 16" – $65.00-30.00; 26" – $125.00-50.00.
Kewty: Composition/molded hair: 10" – $35.00-10.00.

ARRANBEE DOLL COMPANY

Littlest Angel. All hard plastic – 10" – $45.00-12.00; Vinyl head – 10" – $22.00-6.00.

Miss Coty: vinyl: 10" – $35.00-15.00.

My Angel: Plastic/vinyl: 17" – $25.00-8.00; 22" – $50.00-18.00; 36" – $110.00-45.00.

Nancy: Composition: 12" – $100.00-40.00; 17" – $150.00-40.00; 19" – $175.00-50.00; 23" – $195.00-50.00.

Nancy Lee: Composition: 14" – $125.00-45.00; hard plastic: 14" – $125.00-40.00.

Nancy Lee: Unusual eyebrows/vinyl: 15" – $95.00-32.00.

Nancy Lee: Baby, painted eyes and looks as if crying: 15" – $50.00-20.00.

Nanette: H.P.. 14" – $65.00-20.00; 17" – $135.00-35.00; 21" – $150.00-45.00; 23" – $175.00-50.00.

Sonja Skater: Composition: 18" – $140.00-45.00; 21" – $175.00-60.00.

Taffy: Looks like Alexander's "Cissy": 23" – $60.00-28.00.

19" "Nancy". All composition and all original. Open mouth. Courtesy Mary Sweeney. $175.00.

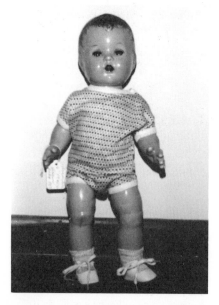

Arranbee composition baby and one of the "Dream Baby" series. Courtesy Jeannie Mauldin. 26" – $125.00.

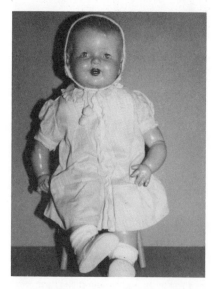

25" "Baby Nancy" Early 1930's. Made to 1939, but later ones have deeper stroke hair and thinner opening in mouth. Cloth body and composition. Courtesy Glorya Woods. 25" – $100.00.

20″ "Nanette". All hard plastic. All original and holds umbrella. Courtesy June Schultz. $150.00.

10″ "Littlest Angel". Hard plastic with vinyl head. Jointed knees. Original. Courtesy Jay Minter. $45.00.

AVERILL, GEORGENE (MADAME HENDRON)

First prices are for mint dolls. Second for crazed, chips, dirty or soiled and not original. Georgene Averill and Madame Hendron are the same person and the business names used by her were: Madame Georgene Dolls, Paul Averill Mfg. Co., Averill Mfg. Co., Georgene Novelties, Madame Hendron and the Brophey Doll Co. in Canada. Georgene Averill began making dolls in 1913 and she designed a great many dolls for George Borgfeldt.

Baby Georgene or Baby Hendron: Composition/cloth: 22″ – $135.00-65.00.

Baby Yawn: Composition/closed eyes/-yawn mouth: 17″ – $250.00-85.00.

Body Twist dolls: Composition with large ball joint at waist: 15″ – $265.00-95.00.

Bonnie Babe: Bisque head/cloth body: 14″ – $650.00; 22″ – $1200.00.

Cloth dolls: Internationals: 15″ – $65.00-25.00; Children: 15″ – $100.00-40.00.

Dolly Dingle: All cloth: 11″-12″ – $225.00-100.00.

Dolly Record: Compo./cloth with record player in back: 26″ – $425.00-150.00.

Googly: Composition/cloth: 14″ – $195.00-85.00; 16″ – $225.00-85.00; 19″ – $300.00-100.00.

Indian, Cowboy: 14″ – $195.00-85.00.

AVERILL, GEORGENE (MADAME HENDRON)
BABY BERRY

Sailor, Soldier: 14″ – $195.00-85.00.
Snookums: Composition/cloth. Comic character: 14″ – $265.00-100.00.
Vinyl head, laughing child with oil cloth body: 28″ – $85.00-45.00.
Whistling Dan (boy), Sailor, Cowboy or Cop: 14″ – $125.00-60.00.
Whistling Rufus (Black): 14″ – $150.00-55.00.

Laughing Child. 28″ with oil cloth body, legs and arms with vinyl head and hands. Dimples. Marks: Georgene Averill, on head. Courtesy Jeannie Mauldin. $85.00.

"Mitze" by Madame Hendron (Georgene Averill). All composition and one of the "body twist" series. Has large ball joint so waist is jointed, molded hair and large painted eyes. Original. Courtesy Kay Bransky. $265.00.

BABY BERRY

First prices are for mint dolls. Second for dolls in poor condition, dirty, soiled or not original.
Alfred E. Newman: vinyl head: 20″ – $95.00-45.00.
Capt. Kangaroo: 19″ – $75.00-25.00; 24″ – $125.00-50.00.
Christopher Robin: 18″ – $65.00-25.00.
Daisy Mae: 14″ – $85.00-45.00; 21″ – $100.00-55.00.

Emmett Kelly (Willie the Clown): 24″ – $95.00-40.00.
Lil' Abner: 14″ – $95.00-45.00; 21″ – $125.00-60.00.
Mammy Yokum: Molded hair: 14″ – $125.00-60.00; 21″ – $150.00-70.00.
Mammy Yokum: Yarn hair: 14″ – $100.00-40.00; 21″ – $125.00-60.00.
Pappy Yokum: 14″ – $125.00-60.00; 21″ – $150.00-70.00.

24″ "Emmett Kelly" as "Willie the Clown". All original, but derby hat missing. Courtesy Mary Tollari. $95.00.

8½″ "Baby Susan". 1958. Sleep eyes, molded hair and open mouth/nurser. Marks: Baby Susan, on head. Made by Marlon Dolls, which also marketed the doll under the name "Sussy" in the early 1960's. "Baby Susan" was marketed through the EEGEE Doll Co. Courtesy Virginia Jones. Mint: $10.00

BETSY McCALL

First prices are for mint dolls. Second for soiled, dirty, played with and not original dolls.

8″ All hard plastic, jointed knees. Made by American Character Doll Co. 8″ street dress – $75.00-35.00; Ballgown – $125.00-45.00.

11¼″ Brown sleep eyes, reddish rooted hair. Unmarked. Made by Uneeda: 11½″ – $45.00-22.00.

13″ Made by Horsman in 1975 although doll is marked: Horsman Dolls, Inc. 1967, on head. 13″ – $35.00-15.00.

14″ All vinyl with rooted hair and medium high heel feet. Made by American Character. 14″ – $125.00-40.00.

14″ Vinyl head, rooted hair. Hard plastic marked P-90 body. Made by Ideal Doll Co. 14″ – $125.00-40.00.

22″ Unmarked. Has extra joints at waist, ankles, wrists and above knees. Made by Uneeda. 22″ – $150.00-60.00.

29″ Marked: McCall 1961. Has extra joints at ankles, waist, above knees and wrists. Made by Uneeda. 29″ – $200.00-95.00.

29″ Marked: B.M.C. Horsman 1971 – $95.00.

BETSY McCALL

36″ Marked: McCall Corp. 1959. Rooted hair. Made by Ideal Doll Co. 36″ – $250.00-125.00.

36″ "Sandy McCall" boy made by Ideal Doll Co. Marked: McCall Corp. 1959. Has molded hair. 36″ – $300.00-150.00.

36″ "Betsy McCall". Plastic and vinyl with blue sleep eyes and rooted hair. Marks: McCall Corp./1959, on head. Courtesy Margaret Weeks. $250.00.

36″ "Sandy McCall". Plastic and vinyl with molded hair, sleep eyes and marked: McCall Corp. 1959. Made by Ideal Doll Co. Courtesy Phyllis Houston. $300.00.

29″ & 22″ "Betsy McCall". 29″ marked: McCall Corp/1961. 22″ unmarked. Both made by Uneeda. Both have extra joints high on upper legs, waist & wrists. Courtesy Jeannie Mauldin. 22″ – $150.00; 29″ – $200.00.

BETSY McCALL

8″ "Betsy McCall". All hard plastic with wig rooted on vinyl cap. Original. Made by American Character Doll Co. $75.00.

14″ "Betsy McCall" with vinyl head and hard plastic marked P-90 body. Made by Ideal Doll Co. Courtesy Jay Minter. $125.00.

11½″ "Betsy McCall". Plastic and vinyl with rooted hair, small sleep eyes and posable head. All original. Doll unmarked. Made by Uneeda Doll Co. $45.00.

BUDDY LEE
CABBAGE PATCH

13" "Buddy Lee". All hard plastic and jointed at shoulders only. Painted features and hair. Marks: Buddy Lee, on back. Original with cap missing. $150.00.

12" "Buddy Lee". All composition with molded hair and painted features. Jointed at shoulders only. Painted-on black shoes. Original. Courtesy Allin Collection. $125.00.

CABBAGE PATCH

Original dolls by Xavier Roberts incorporated as Original Appalachian Artworks in September 1978. The Birth Certificates have a blue border and the 1978 edition is called

"A" **Blue Edition:** Number in edition was 1,000 – $1,500.00 up.

"B" **Red Edition:** Birth Certificates have red border, and these were first to also have adoption papers. (Nov. 1978) – $1,500.00 up.

"C" **Burgundy Edition:** Jan. 1979. Number in edition was 5,000. Registration number has the prefix "C" and they also were first to use three-part adoption papers – $1,000.00 up.

"D" **Purple Edition:** Birth Certificate has purple border. Number in edition was 10,000 which were gone by Novembr 1979 – $900.00.

"X" **Christmas Edition.** 1979: Snow white yarn hair and red costumes. Edge of certificate is leaves and berries. Number in edition is 1,000. "X" prefix on registration number – $1,500.00.

"E" Bronze Edition: This was last of the personally signed limited edition of 1979. Bronze border on Birth Certificate and these babies were sent a Birthday Card from Babyland General. Number in edition was 15,000. This edition started in Dec. 1979 – $900.00.

Signed Preemie Edition: April, 1980 and number was 5,000. This was first of the Preemies and these babies are hand signed – $850.00.

Celebrity Edition-1980: Number of edition was 5,000. All came dressed in jeans and T-shirt which states: "I'm a Little T.V. Celebrity". This was after the Little People were on the T.V. program "Real People". All are hand signed – $650.00.

Christmas Edition - 1980: Number in edition 2,500 and all are hand signed. Birth Certificate has green leaves and red berries border. Babies have white hair and red velveteen outfits – $850.00.

Grand Edition: 1980 and can still be adopted at Babyland General Hospital. Number of edition is 1,000. These Cabbage Patch dolls are dressed in evening attire in tuxedos, satins, mink and diamonds. Each are signed – $1,000.00.

Ears Edition-1981: First babies with ears. Number in edition is 15,000 and these are still available from Babyland General Hospital. This is the first group of babies to have the Xavier Roberts signature STAMPED and is therefore the first "unsigned" edition. Boys have blue and girls have pink Birth Certificates – $350.00.

Unsigned Edition 1980-1981: Number in edition was 73,650. This was first STAMPED rather than personally signed with the Xavier Roberts signature of the Little People – $250.00.

Preemie Edition-1981: Number in edition is 10,000 and these are still available from Babyland General Hospital. This second Preemie edition began in May 1981. Dressed in pastel christening gowns and caps. These babies are STAMPED and not personally signed – $130.00.

Standing Edition-1981: 23″ tall and will stand by themselves. Number in edition is 5,000 and they are still available from Babyland General Hospital. These are STAMPED and not signed personally by Xavier Roberts – $300.00.

Ears Edition-1982: Number in edition is 5,000 with them still available from Babyland General Hospital. Lavender border on Birth Certificate and babies are STAMPED with signature – $140.00.

Unsigned Edition-1982: Number of edition was 21,000 and by Jan. 1984 this edition was adopted out. These are STAMPED and not personally signed – $200.00.

Cabbage Patch Edition-1982: Prior to this edition the babies were called Little People. Edition was numbered at 2,500. This edition was adopted out by mid-1983. There are 10 names used in this edition with a variation of each second name of the 10. For example: Otis L. with the second name differing (beginning with L) for each baby. Edition is STAMPED and have "Cabbage Patch Kids" someplace on clothes – $600.00 up.

Christmas Edition-1982: Number in edition is 1,000. Ribbon border with green leaves and berries on Birth Certificate. The bald head and with-hair babies were used and all are dressed in red. They are STAMPED and HAND SIGNED in red. This is first year the name Cabbage Patch appears on the registration and adoption papers – $1,200.00.

Cleveland Green Edition: Number in edition is 2,000. Began in Jan. 1983 and babies were STAMPED and were all adopted out by Feb. 14, 1983. The Birth Certificates and registration papers have a green border – $600.00.

"KP" Darker Green Edition: Number in edition was 2,000 and began in Feb. 1983 and were all adopted out by spring 1983. STAMPED in green with Xavier Roberts name – $800.00.

"KPR" Red Edition: Number in edition is 2,000 which began in June 1983 and all were adopted out by July, 1983. STAMPED. All papers have a red border – $800.00.

CABBAGE PATCH

"KPB" Burgundy Edition: Number in edition was 10,000 and these were STAMPED. All papers have a burgundy border. Began in Aug. 1983 and all adopted out by Dec. 1983 – $375.00.

Oriental Edition: Number in edition was 1,000. These Cabbage Patch dolls have Oriental looking features and adoption papers have pagoda roofs in yellow on them. Dressed in Oriental style clothes. This was first of the International Series. Began in Mar. 1983 and all adopted by Aug. 1983. STAMPED – $1,000.00.

American Indian Edition: Number of edition was 1,000. These began in June 1983 and were all adopted by Oct. 1983. STAMPED. Skin tones are brown and each is dressed in Indian outfits. 500 girls and 500 boys – $1,000.00.

Hispanic Edition: Number in edition was 1,000. STAMPED. The papers have red roses and the name Cabbage Patch Kids in green in the center top of papers. Edition adopted out in 1983 – $925.00.

Champagne Edition: Number in edition was 2,000. This edition was to celebrate the Fifth Anniversary of the Cabbage Patch. This entire edition was personnally SIGNED by Xavier Roberts. The girls wear lilac with lace trimmings and the boys have lavender short pants. Each has lavender eyes and champagne light beige hair. This edition began in July 1983 and was all adopted out by Feb. 1984 – $1,500.00.

Christmas Edition-1983: The STAMPED edition was numbered at 1,000. Light blonde hair, dressed in reds. All adopted by spring 1984 – $995.00.

"KPP" Purple Edition: Number in edition was 20,000. Papers all have purple borders. STAMPED. These began in Dec. 1983 and were all adopted out by April 1984 – $450.00.

Sweetheart Editon: Number in edition was 1,500 and they were STAMPED. These were available as a couple and dressed in coordinated outfits that were red and white. They were all adopted by Feb. 1984 – $1,000.00.

Bavarian Edition: Number in edition was 1,000 and they were STAMPED. These were the fourth in the International Series

Xavier Roberts "Little People" adopted dolls. This one is "Robert Leon". Made at Babyland Hospital, Georgia. Courtesy Freda Webster.

CABBAGE PATCH

and were all adopted in a two-week period after they were introduced on March 1, 1984. STAMPED. All have blonde hair and blue eyes and are dressed in the Bavarian style – $1,000.00.

World Class Edition: Number in edition was 2,500 and they are STAMPED. Dressed in the Olympic style with running suits, white shorts, head bands and a World Class designed medal on red/white/blue ribbon around neck. First available in May 1984 and edition was adopted rapidly – $650.00.

COLECO CABBAGE PATCH DOLLS:

1983: Black signature stamped. Boxes undated on front. Bald babies – $85.00; Pacifiers – $95.00; Freckles – $100.00; Bald Black Babies – $85.00; Black boys – $75.00; Regular boys or girls – $80.00.

1984: Green signature stamped. Boxes marked 1984 on front. Regular boys or girls – $65.00; Preemies – $55.00; Red loop-haired boy – $85.00; Black Preemie – $60.00; Pacifier – $75.00.

1985: Blue signature stamped. 1985 on front of boxes. Some 1984 dolls are in 1985 boxes and some 1985 dolls are in 1984 boxes. Twins: Regular boys or girls – $85.00; Preemies – $50.00; Black boys or girls – $50.00; Pacifiers – $55.00; Ears – $60.00; Glasses – $85.00; One tooth – $65.00.

Foreign: Germany, Canada, Spain, etc. Freckles – $65.00; Pacifiers – $65.00; Regular boys or girls – $55.00.

"Marie Florence" one of Xavier Roberts "Little People" made at Babyland General Hospital in Georgia. Courtesy Freda Webster.

CABBAGE PATCH

16″ "Shane Roger" signed on neck: Made in Spain. Box in two languages: French and English. Brown eyes, freckles, two dimples, auburn hair and pacifier. Signed in black Sept. 5, 1984. Courtesy Marlowe Cooper.

14″ "Mark Tyrus". One upper tooth, two dimples, bald head, blue eyes and ears. Stamped in blue ink and not dated. Satin label says: Made in China. Courtesy Marlowe Cooper.

16″ "Gale Freda". Dated Oct. 1. Brown pony-tail, brown eyes and two dimples. Signed in green ink and dated 1984. Red leotards and yellow dress. Courtesy Marlowe Cooper.

13″ "Diane Hattie". Birth date of Sept. 1. Bald head, blue eyes, ears and preemie on label. Signed in black ink and date 1984. Pink baby dress with jacket and has matching booties. Courtesy Marlowe Cooper.

14" "Rex Chester". Dated Oct. 1. Bald head baby with blue eyes, two dimples and freckles. Signed in black ink and 1984. Dressed in white sleepers. Courtesy Marlowe Cooper.

22" "Laura Pauline". Babyland General Hospital original. Dated on birth certificate July 2, 1984. Signed (stamped) in green ink. Also stamped on sole of shoe. Courtesy Marlowe Cooper.

CAMEO DOLL COMPANY

Baby Bo Kaye: Composition/cloth. Mint condition: 18" – $475.00; Light craze and nor original:18" – $300.00.

Baby Mine: Vinyl/cloth. Sleep eyes. Mint condition: 16" – $100.00; Slight soil and not original: 16" – $55.00.

Betty Boop: Composition head. Mint condition: 12" – $400.00; Light craze and few chips: 12" – $295.00.

Champ: Composition/freckles. Mint condition: 16" – $525.00; Light craze, not original: 16" – $400.00.

Giggles: Composition, molded loop for ribbon. Mint: 11" – $225.00; 14" – $350.00; Light craze: 11" – $150.00; 14" – $250.00.

Ho-Ho: Plaster in excellent condition: 4" – $45.00; Vinyl in excellent condition: 4" – $15.00.

Joy: Composition. In mint condition: 10" – $250.00; Slight crazing: 10" – $150.00.

Kewpie: See Kewpie section.

Little Annie Rooney: Composition. Mint and original: 16" – $625.00; Slight craze and not original: 16" – $400.00.

Margie: Composition. Mint and original: 6" – $165.00; 10" – $200.00; Slight craze and not original: 6" – $75.00; 10" – $100.00.

Miss Peep: Pin jointed shoulders and hips. Vinyl. Mint and original: 1960's: 18" – $45.00; Black: 18" – $65.00; Slightly soiled and not original: 18" – $28.00; Black: 18" – $32.00.

Miss Peep, Newborn: Plastic and vinyl. Mint and original. 18" – $65.00; Slight soil and not original: 18" – $30.00.

Peanut, Affectionately: Vinyl. Mint and original: 18½" – $90.00; Slight soil and not original: 18½" – $40.00.

Pete the Pup: Composition. Mint: 8" – $175.00; Slight craze: 8" – $125.00.

CAMEO DOLL COMPANY

Pinkie: Composition. Mint and original: 1930's. 10″ – $200.00; Slight craze. 10″ – $100.00; Vinyl and plastic, 1950's – $65.00; Slight soil and not original – $32.00.

Scootles: Composition. Mint and original – $12″ – $325.00; 15″ – $425.00.

Light craze and not original – 12″ – $225.00; 15″ – $300.00.

Composition. SLEEP EYES: Mint. 15″ – $485.00; 21″ – $600.00.

Slight craze. 15″ – $300.00; 21″ – $450.00.

Composition. Black. 15″ – $600.00.

Vinyl. Mint and original. 14″ – $85.00; 27″ – $200.00; Lightly soiled and not original. 14″ – $45.00; 27″ – $95.00.

13″ Black "Scootles". All composition and original. Courtesy Gloyra Woods. $450.00.

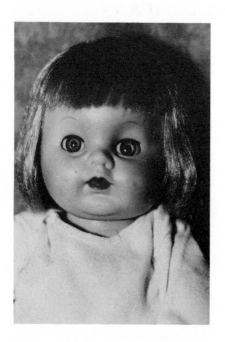

18″ "Plum" on Miss Peep style hinge jointed body. This doll also came with molded hair. The head was also used for "Dyp-A-Babe" in 1956 and as "Affectionately Peanut" in 1958. Courtesy Shirley Merrill. $60.00.

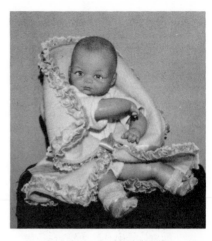

15″ "Miss Peep". All vinyl with pin hinge jointed body. Inset eyes. Courtesy Phyllis Teague. $45.00.

27″ "Scootles". All vinyl with sleep eyes. All orignal. Courtesy Joanna Brunken. $200.00.

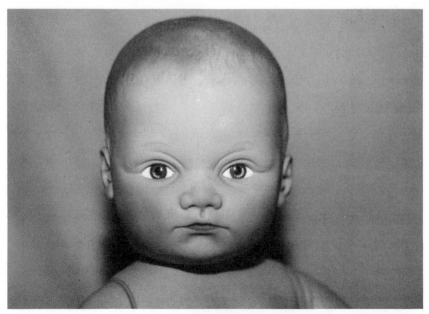

16″ "Newborn Miss Peep". All vinyl. Came on body like "Miss Peep" and also on plastic and vinyl body with jointed wrists. Courtesy Phyllis Teague. $45.00.

COMIC

12" "Betty Boop". 1932. Head is composition as is torso and has jointed wooden arms legs. Shown is black and red painted on clothes, but came in various colors. Courtesy Jackie Barker. $225.00.

14" "Dagwood" and 9" "Alexander". Both all composition and both are marked: Knickerbocker Toy, on heads. Painted features and removable clothes, except the shoes/socks on "Alexander" which are molded and painted. Courtesy Shirley Bertrand. $450.00 up each.

9½" "Pinocchio". Made by Ideal and marked: Disney. Composition. 12" "Clippo Clown" by Effanbee and composition/wood with painted features. 9" "Felix" by Cameo with wooden body and rubber painted head. Courtesy Verna Humphreys. $125.00 each up.

16″ "Deputy Dawg". All flannelette material with printed on features and details. Date and maker unknown. Courtesy Phyllis Houston. $45.00.

18″ "Little Audrey". Cloth with vinyl head, molded hair and painted features. Tag: LIttle Audrey/Harvey Famous Cartoons. Courtesy Alice Capps. $100.00.

21″ "Snow White" and Dwarfs. All early vinyl. Doll marked: Snow White on head and Disney on foot. Set original cost $19.98 and box states: DeLuxe Toy Creations, Inc. N.Y. Courtesy Ann Wencel. Set – $135.00.

COMIC

16″ "Popeye" cloth with vinyl head and arms. Molded on cap and pipe. Marks: King Features, Inc. Popeye. 1960. Made by Eegee Doll Co. Courtesy Jeannie Mauldin. $20.00.

27″ "Lucy" of "I Love Lucy" T.V. show. Plastic face mask, orange yarn hair and rest is cloth. Marks on apron: I love Lucy/Desi. 1953. Courtesy Allin Collection. $150.00.

6½″ & 7½″ First "Snoopy". Marks: United Feature Syndicate. 1958. These first "Snoopy" are very rare and not style of later ones. Courtesy Margaret Mandel. 6½″ – $30.00; 7½″ – $40.00.

18″ "Huckleberry Hound" with vinyl head and hands, plush body and limbs. Late 1950's. Tag: Knickerbocker Toy Co. Courtesy Martha Sweeney. $20.00.

16″ "Mr. Magoo". 1962. Vinyl head and hat, cloth body, felt hands and clothes. Marks: Ideal Toy Corp., 1962 U.P.A. Pictures, Inc. All Rights Reserved, on tag. Courtesy Jeannie Mauldin. $12.00.

16″ "Betty Boop". All cloth with printed features and garter. Loop earrings and removable black dress. Tag: The Original Betty Boop rag doll/Copyright King Features Syndicate Inc./Colorforms. Courtesy Jeannie Mauldin. $18.00.

CLOTH DOLLS

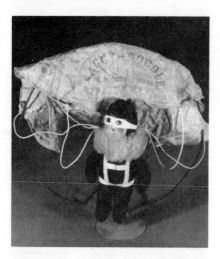

7". "Parachute Jumper, W.W. II". Real fur around neck, oil cloth stitched head, helmet, face mask. Separate goggles. Marks: Raggy-Doodle/U.S./Parachute Trooper/Design Patent Allowed. $45.00.

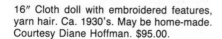

16" Cloth doll with embroidered features, yarn hair. Ca. 1930's. May be home-made. Courtesy Diane Hoffman. $95.00.

12" Marks: The Doll with a thousand faces/Pat. Dec. 26, 1939, Other Pat. Pend./The Expression Doll Co./Dallas Texas. Body is wood stick and when turned makes the expression on the cloth face change. Courtesy Jean Couch. $65.00.

16″ "Snow White". Cloth and oil cloth with painted features. Maker unknown. Courtesy Kathy Feagans. $50.00.

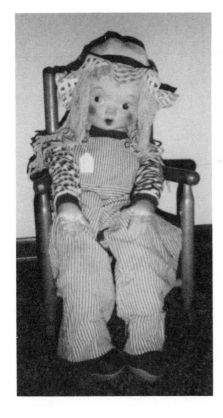

40″ Cloth doll with mask face, painted features, yarn hair, felt feet. Ca. 1940's and early 1950's. Courtesy Jeannie Mauldin. $45.00.

14″ "Sarah From Hawaii". All cloth with stitched features. Plastic lea and flower in hair. 1972. Courtesy Wendi Miller. $10.00.

DELUXE TOY COMPANY

All prices are for mint dolls. Deluxe Reading, Deluxe Topper, Topper Corp., Topper Toys, Deluxe Toy Creations are all the same company with the "parent" compnay being Deluxe Toys. None of the above named remain in business.

Deluxe Toy Company specialized in dolls that "do things", or as referred to as mechanical dolls. The quality of their dolls were good to excellent. Most dolls are fully marked with the name of the company and the date. They made regular dolls as well as the mechanical and almost all the dolls from these firms are becoming very desirable and also hard to find.

Baby Brite: two buttons in stomach to move head and arms: 14" – $15.00.

Baby Boo: Battery operated: 21" – $20.00.

Baby Catch A Ball: Battery operated. Metal bracelets at wrists: 18" – $20.00.

Baby Magic: Button in stomach operated arms and mouth: 18" – $25.00.

Baby Peek and Play: Battery operated. Jointed wrists, hides eyes: 18" – $20.00.

Baby Tickle Tears: Painted eyes. Arms make mouth pout: 14" – $20.00.

Bikey: Battery operated. Rides bike, jointed knees: 11" – $12.00.

Bonnie Bride: Button on shoulder makes arm toss bouquet and legs walk: 22" – $20.00.

DAWN Series: 6" Girls: White – $6.00; Black – $9.00; Majorettes – $12.00.

Boys: White – $12.00; Black – $12.00; Models – $15.00.

Go Go's: 6½" – $9.00.

Lil' Miss Fussy: Battery operated. Cries and kicks: 18" – $20.00.

Party Time: Battery operated. Blows balloons and noise makers: 18" – $20.00.

Penny Brite: 9" – $8.00.

School Girl Writing Doll: Battery operated. Arms move in all directions. 16" – $25.00.

Smarty Pants: Battery operated talker: 19" – $25.00.

Susie Cutie: Press stomach and arms and mouth move: 7" – $8.00.

Susie Homemaker: Jointed knees: 21" – $25.00.

6½" "Brenda Brush" of the Go-Go's. Posable all vinyl body and limbs made in one piece. Others in set: "Cool Cat", "Slick Chick", "Hot Canary", "Tomboy", "Yeah, Yeah", "Swinger", "Private Ida". Courtesy Mary Sena. $90.00 each.

6½" "Yeah, Yeah" and "Slick Chick" of the Go-Go's. All vinyl that is wired through limbs so they are posable. 1966. Both are original. $9.00 each.

21" "Baby Boo". Battery operated. Marks: Deluxe Reading/1965/68, on head. Courtesy Phyllis Teague. $20.00.

DOLL ARTIST

All prices are for mint dolls.

Clear, Emma: Blue Scarf: 20" – $375.00; Chinas: 20" – $200.00; 26" – $300.00; Danny Boy: 20" – $300.00; Lady Guenevere: 20" – $195.00; "Parian": 16" – $185.00; Washington, George or Martha: 20" – $900.00 pair.

Kane, Maggie Head: Caldonia: 14" – $125.00; Marigold: 14" – $200.00; Nicodemus: 13" – $125.00; Peach Blossom: 14" – $200.00; Uncle Ned: 15" – $150.00.

Wilson, Lita: Cinderella: 16" – $250.00; Girls: 16" – $200.00; Boys: 16" – $250.00.

16" "Parthenia" "Parian" by Emma Clear. Deep curls in back with ribbon. Cloth body with "parian" lower limbs. Pierced ears. Marks: Clear with a '46 inside the C. $185.00

DOLL ARTIST

25" China with flat top hairdo and sausage curls around head. China glaze has a pink luster. Marked: Clear with '46 in the C. $250.00.

Original character dolls by Faith Wick. Late 1970's. Courtesy Faith Wick. $650.00 up.

Original design "Indian Maid" in cloth and porcelain by Faith Wick. Late 1970's. Courtesy Faith Wick. $640.00 up.

16″ "Eskimo" made by Arlene Wacker. All cloth and felt. Courtesy Arlene Wacker. $125.00.

13″ "Pouty Shirley Temple". Designed and made by Karen Bauser. Composition head, cloth body and felt arms and legs. Courtesy Glorya Woods. $300.00 up.

DOLL ARTIST
DUTCHESS DOLLS

12" "Betty Boop". All composition with jointed arms and legs. 6" All bisque in front. Made by Marjorie Dean and marked: M.D. Courtesy Glorya Woods. $65.00 up.

12" "Lil Witch" and "Hannibal" the Bat. Original by owner Phyllis Teague. $60.00 up.

DUTCHESS DOLLS

All prices are for mint dolls.

Dolls from the Dutchess Company will be marked: Duchess Doll, low on the back or Dutchess Doll Corp./copyright/1948. They are all hard plastic with jointed neck and shoulders, but the body and legs are made in one piece with painted, molded on shoes. They can have painted eyes or sleep eyes. All have mohair wigs or painted hair. Dolls of this type were sold from 1948 throughout the 1950's from catalog houses and "dime" stores across the nation. A great many of them are still around and will be seen at almost every antique show or Mall show. The clothes are stapled on. This style

doll is not too desirable by the collector, but due to the amount seen wherever items are sold, they are included here.

Carmen: 7½" – $3.00.
Cinderella: 7½" – $4.00.
Groom: 7½" – $6.00.
Months, Birthday: 7½" – $3.00.
Peter Pan: 7½" – $6.00.
Pricilla: 7½" – $3.00.
Roy Rogers or Dale Evans: 7½" – $6.00.
Scarlett: 7½" – $3.00.
Scotch Miss: 7½" – $3.00.
Tinkerbelle: $6.00.

214

DUTCHESS DOLLS

7½" "March". Sleep eyes, all hard plastic. Stapled-on clothes. 1950. $3.00.

7½" "November". Sleep eyes, all hard plastic. Stapled-on clothes. 1950. $3.00.

7½" "Pricilla". Sleep eyes, all hard plastic. Stapled-on clothes. 1949. $3.00.

EEGEE DOLL COMPANY

The name of this company is made up from the name of the founder, E.G. Goldberger. Founded in 1917, the early dolls were marked: E.G., then later, E.Goldberger and now Eegee.

Andy: Plastic/vinyl teen boy. 12″ – $22.00.
Annette: Teen type. 11½″ – $22.00.
Annette: Plastic and vinyl, walker legs: 25″ – $32.00; 28″ – $40.00; 36″ – $60.00.
Baby Luv: Cloth/vinyl. Marks: B.T. Eegee: 14″ – $40.00.
Baby Susan: Name marked on head: 8½″ – $10.00.
Baby Tandy Talks: Foam Body, rest vinyl. Pull string talker – $50.00.
Ballerina: Foam body and limbs. Vinyl head. 18″ – $32.00.
Ballerina: Hard plastic/vinyl: 20″ – $38.00.
Boy doll: Molded hair, all vinyl: 13″ – $27.00; 21″ – $35.00.
Debutante: Vinyl head, rest hard plastic/jointed knees: 28″ – $85.00.
Dolly Pardin: 1980. 12″ – $16.00.
Flowerkins: Plastic/vinyl. Marks: F-2, on head. 16″ – $35.00 each.
Gemmette: Teen type. 14″ – $16.00.
Georgette and Georgie: Cloth & vinyl. Redheads: 22″-23″ – $25.00 each.
Gigi Perreaux: Hard plastic/early vinyl head: 17″ – $150.00.
Granny from Beverly Hillbillies: Old lady modeling, grey hair. Painted or sleep eyes: 14″ – $55.00.
Miss Charming: All composition Shirley Temple look-a-like: 19″ – $185.00.
Musical Baby: Has key wind music box in body: 17″ – $18.00.
My Fair Lady: All vinyl, jointed waist: 19″ – $45.00; 10½″ – $20.00.
Posey Playmate: Foam and vinyl: 18″ – $16.00.
Susan Stroller: Hard plastic and vinyl: 20″ – $45.00; 23″ – $55.00; 26″ – $65.00.
Tandy Talks: Plastic, vinyl, freckles, pull string talker: 20″ – $60.00.

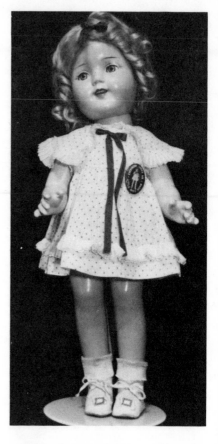

19″ "Miss Charming". Shirley Temple look-a-like. All composition with mohair wig. Original clothes and pin. Courtesy Martha Sweeney. $185.00.

16″ "Susan Stroller". Hard plastic body and limbs with jointed knees. Vinyl head, rooted hair. Original. Marks: Eegee, on head and back. Courtesy Jeannie Mauldin. $40.00.

18″ Ballerina. One-piece foam body and limbs with vinyl hands and head. Rooted hair, blue body suit and tutu. Marks: Eegee/1967, on head. $32.00.

12″ "Baby Luv". Cloth with vinyl head and limbs. Large painted eyes. Marks: 14BT/-Eegee Co. 1973. Courtesy Jeannie Mauldin. $30.00.

EFFANBEE DOLL COMPANY

First prices are for mint dolls. Second for soiled, dirty, played with dolls, or composition, crazed or cracked.

American Children: All composition. Painted or sleep eyes. Closed mouth girl: 18" – $800.00-400.00; 21" – $1,000.00-500.00.

Closed mouth boy: 15" – $800.00-400.00; 17" – $1,000.00-500.00.

Open mouth: 15" – $600.00-300.00; 18" – $675.00-300.00; 21" – $800.00-400.00.
Anne Shirley: All composition. 15" – $165.00-95.00; 21" – $235.00-100.00; 27" – $345.00-150.00.
Babyette: Cloth/composition. 12½" – $150.00-85.00.
Babykin: All composition. 9"-12" – $150.00-85.00. All vinyl: 10" – $45.00-20.00.
Baby Cuddleup. Vinyl coated cloth body, rest vinyl. Two lower teeth. 1953. 20" – $60.00-30.00.
Baby Dainty: Composition/cloth. 15" – $145.00-85.00.
Baby Evelyn: Composition/cloth. 17" – $165.00-85.00.
Baby Tinyette: Composition: 8" – $145.00-65.00; Toddler: 8" – $145.00-65.00.
Bi-Centennial boy and girl (Pun'kin). 11" – $125.00 each-45.00 each.
Bridal Sets: 1970's-4 dolls. White – $185.00-100.00; Black – $300.00-150.00.
Bright Eyes: Composition/cloth. Flirty eyes. 18" – $165.00-80.00.
Brother or Sister: Composition hands and head. Yarn hair and painted eyes: 12" – $145.00-50.00; 16" – $175.00-60.00.
Bubbles: Composition/cloth. 16" – $175.00-95.00; 20" – $200.00-100.00; 26" – $300.00-150.00.
Button-nose: Composition. 8"-9" – $135.00-60.00. Vinyl/cloth: 18" – $50.00-20.00.
Candy Kid: All composition. White: 12" – $175.00-70.00; Black: 12" – $250.00-85.00.
Carolina made for Smithsonian. 1980: 12" – $65.00-30.00.

Charlie McCarthy: Composition/cloth. 19"-20" – $235.00-100.00.
Cinderella. All hard plastic. 16" – $175.00-95.00.
Currier & Ives: Plastic/vinyl: 12" – $65.00-30.00.
Disney Dolls, Cinderella, Snow White, Alice in Wonderland and Sleeping Beauty: 1977-1978. 14" – $145.00-65.00.
DyDee Baby: Hard plastic/vinyl. 15" – $85.00-35.00; 20" – $100.00-50.00.
Fluffy: All vinyl: 10" – $35.00-10.00. As Girl Scout: 10" – $45.00-10.00. Black – $45.00-10.00.
Grumpy: Cloth/composition. 12" – $150.00-60.00; 18" – $225.00-85.00. Black: 12" – $225.00-85.00.
Historical Dolls: All composition: 14" – $450.00-125.00; 21" – $1,100.00-500.00.
Honey: All hard plastic: 14" – $100.00-40.00; 18" – $150.00-55.00; 21" – $250.00-80.00.
Ice Queen: Skating outfit. All composition, open mouth: 17" – $675.00-250.00.
Lambkin: Composition/cloth character baby: 16" – $275.00-125.00.
Limited Edition Club Dolls: 1975, Precious Baby – $450.00; 1976, Patsy – $300.00; 1977, Dewees Cochran – $175.00; 1978, Crowning Glory – $250.00; 1979, Skippy – $200.00; 1980, Susan B. Anthony – $150.00; 1981, Girl With Watering Can – $150.00; 1982, Princess Diane – $125.00; 1983, Sherlock Holmes – $145.00; 1984, Bubbles – $90.00.
Little Lady: All composition. 15" – $145.00-65.00; 21" – $195.00-85.00; 27" – $350.00-100.00. Cloth body/yarn hair: 21" – $185.00-95.00.
Lovums: Composition/cloth. 15" – $165.00-80.00; 22" – $225.00-100.00.
Mae Starr: Composition/cloth. Record player in torso: 30" – $425.00-125.00.
Marionettes: Composition/wood. 14" – $125.00-65.00.
Martha Washington: 1976. 11" – $75.00-40.00.
Mary Ann or Lee: Composition/cloth and all composition: 16" – $165.00; 18" – $185.00-90.00; 24" – $225.00-100.00.

EFFANBEE DOLL COMPANY

Mary Jane: Plastic/vinyl, walker & freckles: 31″ – $165.00-80.00.
Mickey: Composition/cloth. Flirty eyes: 18″ – $165.00-80.00.
Mickey: All vinyl. Some with molded hats: 11″ – $95.00-30.00.
Patricia: All composition: 14″ – $225.00-100.00.
Patsy: All composition: 14″ – $225.00-100.00; Composition/cloth: 14″ – $250.00-100.00.
Patsyette: 9″ – $165.00-80.00.
Patsy Ann: 19″ – $275.00-125.00; Vinyl: 15″ – $95.00-45.00.
Patsy Joan: 16″ – $250.00-100.00.
Patsy Jr.: 11″ – $200.00-85.00.
Patsy Lou: 22″ – $325.00-150.00.
Patsy Mae: 30″ – $475.00 up-185.00.
Patsy Ruth: 26″-27″ – $475.00 up-185.00.
Patsy, Wee: 5″-6″ – $250.00-100.00.
Polka-Dottie: 21″ – $150.00-80.00.
Portrait Dolls: All composition. 12″ – $165.00 each-55.00.
Prince Charming: All hard plastic. 16″ – $195.00-95.00.
Rootie Kazootie: 21″ – $165.00-55.00.
Rosemary: Composition/cloth: 14″ – $165.00-80.00; 22″ – $250.00-100.00; 28″ – $350.00-125.00.
Skippy: All composition. 14″ – $250.00-100.00.

Sunny Toddler: Plastic/vinyl. 18″ – $65.00-30.00.
Suzanne: All composition. 14″ – $150.00-65.00.
Suzette: All composition. 12″ – $135.00-60.00.
Sweetie Pie: Composition/cloth. 14″ – $125.00-65.00; 19″ – $150.00-75.00; 24″ – $200.00-95.00.
Tommy Tucker: Composition/cloth. Flirty eyes. 18″ – $165.00-80.00.
W.C. Fields: Composition/cloth. 22″ – $695.00-200.00; Plastic/vinyl. 15″ – $175.00-80.00.

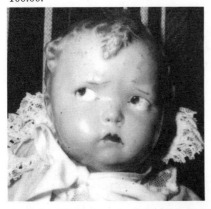

14″ "Grumpy" marked: 176. Cloth and composition with painted eyes. Courtesy June Schultz. $175.00.

22″ "Rosemary". Cloth body with composition head and limbs. All original. Courtesy Jay Minter. $250.00.

219

EFFANBEE DOLL COMPANY

27″ Composition shoulder head with composition arms and legs. Stuffed cloth body.Sleep eyes and mohair wig. Marks: Effanbee, on back of shoulder. Original romper tagged: Patsy Rompers/Pat. Nov. 19, 1918. Tag is on back inside. Courtesy Bonnie Stewart. $200.00.

24″ "Lovums". Cloth with composition head and shoulderplate and limbs. Caracul wig. Open mouth with two upper and lower teeth. Courtesy Joleen Flack. $250.00.

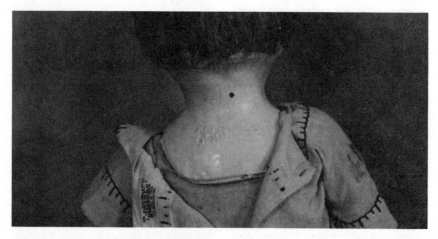

Tag on back of rompers inside: Patsy Rompers/Pat. Nov. 19, 1918. Courtesy Bonnie Stewart.

EFFANBEE DOLL COMPANY

22″ "Patsy Lou". All composition and original with skates attached to one arm. The bag of marbles were added. Courtesy Jay Minter. $325.00.

9″ "Patsyette". All composition and original with N.R.A. tag on dress. 1930's. Courtesy Shirley Merrill. $165.00.

14″ "Anne Shirley". All composition and original with paper tag tied to wrist. Blonde wig in braids. Uses the mark: Patricia doll. Courtesy Joanna Brunken. $165.00 up.

EFFANBEE DOLL COMPANY

11″ "Patsy Baby" and marked on head and body. Magnetic hands. All original with card from original box. Holds rattle, flag, teething ring, bottle and ball. Courtesy Billie McCabe. $200.00.

18″ "Little Lady". All composition with human hair wig, sleep eyes. Redressed. Marks: Effanbee/USA, on back. Courtesy Lilah Beck. $145.00.

18″ "Mickey, Bright Eyes or Tommy Tucker". All composition with flirty eyes and caracul wig. Same doll used for all three names. Redressed. Courtesy Jeannie Mauldin. $165.00.

9" "Baby Patsyette". All composition with sleep eyes and caracul wigs. All original clothes. Courtesy Turn of Century Antiques. $165.00.

8" "Babykin". All vinyl, rooted hair, sleep eyes and nurser open mouth. Marks: Effanbee. 1964, on head. Courtesy Shirley Merrill. $45.00.

1976 Limited Edition Club doll "Patsy". Plastic and vinyl. All original. Sleep eyes and molded hair. Fully marked. $300.00.

FISHER-PRICE
FLANDERS

16" "Mandy" by Fisher Price. Marked on head: P0141-1970. In "Patio Party Denim" with denim skirt and calico bodice and trim. Courtesy Susan Crowsey. $18.00.

16" Fisher Price's "Mandy" in discontinued outfit: Sleighride Ensemble". Brown corduroy with "fur" trim. Courtesy Susan Crowsey. $18.00.

FLANDERS

16" Harriet Flanders doll and so marked on head. All composition with molded hair, brown sleep eyes and character face. Courtesy Jeannie Mauldin. $65.00.

10″ Painted ceramic type material. Painted features and marked: Bili/Industria/Argentina. Not original. Courtesy Shirley Merrill. $35.00.

15″ "Coronation Queen" using the Barbara Ann Scott doll. Made by Reliable of Canada. Banner reads: Her Highness Coronation Doll. Courtesy Diane Hoffman. $350.00 up.

10″ Plastic with viny arms, eyes painted to side. Box: Made in the People's Republic (China). No marks on doll. These also come in a composition style material and all are currently available and have been made since 1978. Courtesy Treasure Trove. $28.00.

FOREIGN DOLLS

12″ Boy and girl in original box. All hard plastic in original costumes. Made by Roddy of England. Courtesy Diane Hoffman. $45.00.

11½″ "Sindy" made by Pedigree of England. The English version is identical to American version except it has sleep eyes. $20.00.

14″ Girl of Britanny. Extremely fine clothes which are removable. All vinyl, sleep eyes and rooted hair. Made by Poupees et Creations Reginales of France under the company name: Phillippe. 1978. $48.00.

12″ Sculptured man and women of Normandy made by Atelier D'Art of Saint-Brieuc, France. $37.50.

22″ French celluloid with flirty eyes and dressed in extremely fine quality velvet and brocade outfit. Courtesy Beth & Carole Noi. $60.00.

6½″ Boy and girl made in Germany. Came in celluloid and rigid plastic. Dressed in National costumes. Courtesy Diane Hoffman. $18.00.

FOREIGN DOLLS

12″ Girl from Greece. Composition style material head with painted features. Very ornate clothes. Courtesy Mary Williams. $26.00.

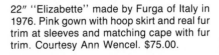

22″ "Elizabette" made by Furga of Italy in 1976. Pink gown with hoop skirt and real fur trim at sleeves and matching cape with fur trim. Courtesy Ann Wencel. $75.00.

14″ "Flic" by Furga. 1970. All original. Plastic and vinyl with cryer box in back. Courtesy Marjorie Uhl. $40.00.

14″ "Tina" by Furga, Italy. Earyl 1950's painted plastic with sleep eyes and original clothes. $45.00.

9½″ All cloth, painted features, all original and hand made in India. Courtesy Mrs. Frank Miller. $12.00.

11″ All cloth man from India. Painted features, all original and handmade. Courtesy Mrs. Frank Miller. $14.00.

FOREIGN DOLLS

4″ Japanese boy and girl in original wicker case. Heads, hands and feet are made of crushed oyster shell paste. Set glass eyes. Original. Courtesy Diane Hoffman. $22.00.

6″ Japanese bisque head with sleep eyes, squeeker stomach, painted shoes. Purchased new in 1970. Original. Marks: Courtesy Renie Culp. $16.00.

17″ Japanese figure made of crushed oyster shell paste and wire armature, representing a dancer. Courtesy Renie Culp. $20.00.

9" Mexico girl of all composition, floss hair and painted features. Jointed at shoulders and hips. Skirt stamped: Aqui Michu. Courtesy Penny Pendlebury. $10.00.

8" Pressed, oil painted head and wire/cloth armature body and limbs. Tag: Creaciones Goya Made in Spain. These same style dolls were made by Klumpe of Spain also. $45.00.

7", 4½" & 3" All wood nesting dolls from Russia. One fits over the others. All painted bright colors. Courtesy Mrs. Frank Miller. $18.00.

HASBRO

All prices are for mint dolls.

Adam: 1971. Boy of World of Love series. 9" – $12.00.

Aimee: 1972. Plastic & vinyl. 18" – $40.00.

Defender: One-piece arms and legs. 1974. 11½" – $10.00.

Dolly Darling: 1965. 4½" – $6.00.

Flying Nun: Plastic & vinyl. 1967. 5" – $15.00.

G.I. Joe: Flocked or molded hair, no beard. 1964. 12" – $30.00.

Flocked hair and beard. 12" – $22.50

Eagle eyes. 1975. 11½" – $15.00.

Talking: 11½" – $22.50.

Foreign, includes: Australian, Japanese, German, Russian – $75.00 each.

Nurse: 11" – $125.00 up.

Leggy: 10" – $8.00.

Little Miss No Name. 1965. 15" – $60.00.

Monkees. (Set of four). 4" – $30.00.

Storybooks. 1967. 3" – $9.00 each.

Sweet Cookie: 1972. 18" – $15.00.

That Kid. 1967. 21" – $65.00.

World of Love Dolls. 1968. 9" – $8.00 each.

12" "Japanese" with very Oriental face modeling. Original uniform. $75.00.

"Russian" G.I. Joe with original uniform and different face modeling than regular G.I. Joes. $75.00.

12″ Early G.I. Joe sailor. Has flocked hair and no beard. $30.00.

Foreign G.I. Joe "German" with different face modeling and German uniform. $75.00.

4″ "Mama's And The Papas". Left to right: Cass Elliot, Denny Daheaty and Michelle Gillian. All marked 1967 and came with a 33⅓ record telling about person. Courtesy Virginia Jones. $30.00 each.

HASBRO
HORSMAN DOLL COMPANY

9″ "Bonnie Blue Belle". All composition with painted features. Glued on mohair wig. Marks: Hollywood Doll, on back. Original. 1945. Courtesy Earlene Johnston. $18.00.

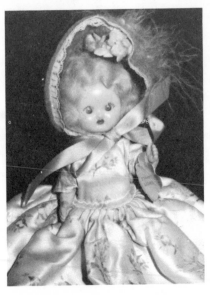

5½″ "Sweet Janice". All hard plastic with glued on mohair wig. Sleep eyes and original. Marks: Hollywood Doll, in star on back. Wrist tag: Sweet Janice/Hollywood Doll, in star. 1950. $12.00.

HORSMAN DOLL COMPANY

First prices are for mint dolls. Second for dolls that may be crazed, cracked, soiled, dirty or not original.

Answer Doll. Buttons in back make head move. 1966. 10″ – $10.00-5.00.

Billiken. Composition head, slant eyes, plush or velvet body. 1909. 12″ – $275.00-100.00.

Baby Bumps: Composition & cloth. 1910. 11″ – $135.00-65.00; 16″ – $165.00-85.00. Black: 11″ – $185.00-85.00; 16″ – $225.00-100.00.

Baby First Tooth: Cloth & vinyl, cry mouth, one tooth, tears on cheeks. 16″ – $40.00-20.00.

Baby Tweaks: Cloth & vinyl. Inset eyes. 1967. 20″ – $32.50-16.00.

Bedknobs & Broomsticks. Came with plastic and tin bed. Doll has jointed waist, painted eyed. 6½″ – $12.00-6.00.

Betty: All composition. 16″ – $95.00-45.00; Plastic & vinyl: 16″ – $18.00-9.00.

Betty Jo: All composition: 16″ – $95.00-45.00; Plastic & vinyl: 16″ – $18.00-9.00.

Betty Ann: All composition: 19″ – $95.00-45.00; Plastic & vinyl: 19″ – $18.00-9.00.

Betty Jane: All composition: 25″ – $125.00-85.00; Plastic & vinyl: 25″ – $40.00-20.00.

Betty Jane: All composition: 25″ – $125.00-85.00; Plastic & vinyl: 25″ – $40.00-20.00.

Betty Bedtime: All composition: 16″ – $95.00-45.00; 20″ – $125.00-65.00.

Body Twist: All composition. Top of body fits down into the torso. 11″ – $100.00-40.00.

Bright Star. All hard plastic. Open mouth. 1952. 15″ – $90.00-40.00.

Brother: Composition/cloth: 22″ – $95.00-35.00; Vinyl: 13″ – $25.00-10.00.

Celeste Portrait Doll: In frame. Eyes painted to side: 12″ – $20.00-10.00.

Christopher Robin: 11″ – $32.00-15.00.

Child Dolls: All composition: 15″ – $95.00-40.00; 19″ – $125.00-60.00.

Al hard plastic: 14″ – $50.00-25.00; 18″ – $65.00-28.00.

Cindy: All hard plastic. 1950's: 15″ – $50.00-25.00; 17″ – $65.00-30.00.

All early vinyl: 15″ – $25.00-15.00; 18″ – $40.00-20.00.

Lady type: Swivel waist: 19″ – $45.00-20.00.

Cinderella: Plastic/vinyl. Painted eyes to side: 11½″ – $18.00-8.00.

Country Girl: 9″ – $12.00-5.00.

Crawling Baby: Vinyl. 1967: 14″ – $28.00-12.00.

Dimples, Baby: Composition/cloth: 20″ – $175.00-65.00; 24″ – $200.00-85.00.

Toddler: 20″ – $185.00-75.00; 24″ – $225.00-95.00.

Laughing, painted teeth: 22″ – $245.00-100.00.

Gold Medal Doll: Composition/cloth, upper and lower teeth: 21″ – 95.00-40.00.

Vinyl, molded hair: 26″ – $150.00-65.00.

Ella Cinders: Comic character. Composition/cloth: 14″ – $275.00-100.00; 18″ – $495.00-180.00.

Flying Nun: (Patty Duke). 1965. 12″ – $45.00-20.00.

Hebee-Shebee: All composition: 10½″ – $90.00 each-40.00.

Jackie Coogan: Composition/cloth. 14″ – $425.00-185.00.

Jackie Kennedy: Plastic/vinyl: 1961 – 25″ – $95.00-35.00.

Jeanie Horsman: All composition: 14″ – $100.00-45.00.

Composition/cloth: 16″ – $100.00-45.00.

JOJO: All composition: 12″ – $75.00-35.00.

Life Size Baby: Plastic/vinyl: 26″ – $150.00-70.00.

Lullabye Baby: Cloth/vinyl. Music box: 12″ – $18.00; All vinyl: 12″ – $12.00-5.00.

Mary Poppins: 12″ – $25.00-10.00; 16″ – $45.00-20.00; 26″ – $100.00-50.00.

Mama Style Babies: Composition/cloth: 16″ – $85.00-30.00; 22″ – $100.00-60.00.

Hard plastic/cloth: 16″ – $65.00-30.00; 22″ – $90.00-40.00.

Vinyl/cloth: 16″ – $20.00-8.00; 22″ – $30.00-15.00.

Peggy Pen Pal: Multi jointed arms. Plastic/vinyl: 18″ – $30.00-12.00.

Pippi Longstockings: Vinyl/cloth: 1972. 18″ – $25.00-14.00.

Pipsqueaks: four in set. 1967: 12″ – $15.00-6.00 each.

Polly & Pete: Black dolls, molded hair: 13″ – $100.00-45.00 each.

Poor Pitiful Pearl: 12″ – $25.00-12.00; 17″ – $45.00-20.00.

Peterkin: All composition, painted googly style eyes: 12″ – $145.00-65.00.

Roberta: All composition. 1937. 14″ – $100.00-45.00; 20″ – $150.00-65.00.

Ruthie: All vinyl or plastic & vinyl: 14″ – $12.00-6.00; 20″ – $22.00-10.00.

Ruthie's Sister: Plastic & vinyl. 1960's. 26″ – $65.00-30.00.

Sleepy Baby: Vinyl & cloth, eyes molded closed: 24″ – $35.00-15.00.

Tessie Talks: Plastic/vinyl: 18″ – $20.00-10.00.

Tuffie: All vinyl. Upper lip molded over lower: 16″ – $42.50-20.00.

HORSMAN DOLL COMPANY

14″ "Jackie Coogan". Cloth body and legs, composition shoulder head, lower arms and has molded hair. Features are painted. All original. Tag: Jackie Coogan Kid Licensed by Jackie Coogan Patent Pending., on pants. Shoulder marked: E.I.H. Co. 1921. Courtesy Jeanne Mauldin. $425.00 up.

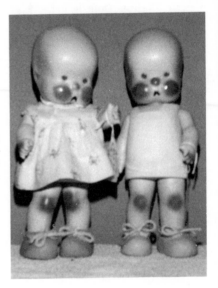

10½″ All composition 1925 "Shebee and Hebee". She has pink and he has blue molded on booties. Her original dress is tagged: Horsman. Jointed shoulder and hips. Courtesy Jeannie Mauldin. $90.00 up.

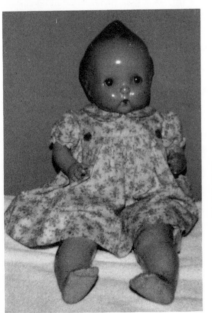

22″ "Sister". Cloth body with composition arms, leg and head with molded hair, sleep eyes and tiny closed mouth. Marks: Sister 1937/Horsman. Courtesy Jeannie Mauldin. $95.00 up.

18" "Baby Chubby". Composition head and rest cloth stuffed. Yarn wig. 1943. Molded hair girl is a "grumpy" type, unmarked and sitting are two character babies, also unmarked. Courtesy Turn of Century Antiques. All: $135.00 each.

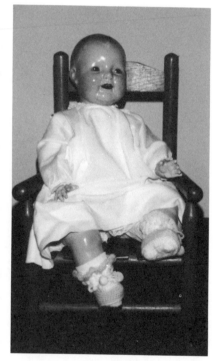

24" "Dimples" with cloth body and composition head and limbs. Open, smiling mouth. Molded hair and marked: E.I. Horsman, on head. Courtesy Jeannie Mauldin. $200.00.

12" "Peterkin" of 1915. All original Indian. Composition and cloth with molded hair and painted features. Closed watermelon painted mouth. Horse is Steiff's "Freudy". Courtesy Kay Bransky. $145.00 up.

HORSMAN DOLL COMPANY

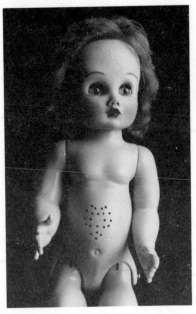

23" "Ruthie Walker" of 1955. All hard plastic body with pin jointed hips and holes in chest. Vinyl head with rooted hair. Some marked 85, on head and others Horsman. Courtesy Betty Wood. $45.00.

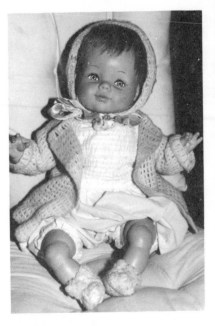

22" "Baby Tweaks". Cloth and vinyl with rooted hair and inset eyes. Squeekers in both legs. Marks: Horsman Dolls Inc./1967/07181, on head. Courtesy Nancy Catlin. $35.00.

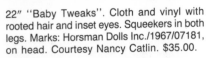

10½" Christopher Robin and 3" Winnie the Pooh. All original in original box. He is plastic and vinyl with rooted hair, painted features and marked: Horsman Doll, Inc. "Pooh" is marked: 1964 Disney Prod. Courtesy Jeannie Mauldin. $32.00.

HORSMAN DOLL COMPANY

12″ "Celeste" in picture frame box. Ornately dressed plastic and vinyl doll with rooted hair and eyes painted to sides. Marks: Horsman, on head. Courtesy Marie Ernst. $20.00.

15″ "Mary Poppins" of 1965 in her original box. Sleep eyes. Marked Horsman, on head. Courtesy Turn of Century Antiques. $45.00.

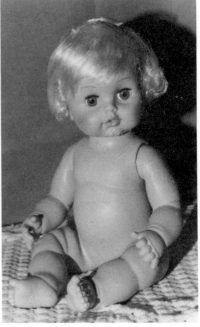

18″ "Lively Baby". All vinyl, sleep eyes and rooted hair. Marks: Horsman Doll, Inc./1972, on head. Horsman Dolls, Inc./15 11H, on back. Courtesy Phyllils Teague. $12.00.

HOWDY DOODY

Prices are for mint dolls.

Howdy Doody Doll (not a puppet). Cloth body with composition head and hands: 17″ – $85.00; 23″ – $125.00.

Puppet (Mouth moves 7 limbs attached to strings). 14″ – $50.00.

Marionette (Mouth moves). Sleep eyes, cloth with hard plastic head and hands. Marked: Ideal Doll: 14″ – $50.00; 20″ – $75.00.

All vinyl: Molded in one piece: 12½″ – $22.00.

All vinyl, jointed at shoulders, hips and neck: 14″ – $30.00.

All cloth: Printed on clothes and features: 16″ – $45.00.

12½″ "Howdy Doody". All vinyl with molded clothes and painted features. One-piece squeeker style doll. Unmarked. Made by Miller Rubber Co. in 1949. $12.00.

Composition head. 17″ "Howdy Doody", 10″ Mask face googly, 12″ Alexander "Dopey", cloth and composition and Horsman's "Bilikin" with plush body and composition material head. Courtesy Turn of Century Antiques. $95.00.

14" All composition with painted eyes to the side. Made during World War II and after. Original pattern used to make majorette costume. Marks: The/Mary Hoyer/Doll, on back. 14" Mint – $225.00; 14" craze & soiled and not original – $95.00.

14" Hoyer doll dressed using Mary Hoyer yarns and called "Peggy" in pattern booklet. Three-piece outfit plus purse and hat. All composition doll with sleep eyes and glued on wig. Marks: The/Mary Hoyer/Doll, on back. 1947. 14" Mint – $225.00; 14" Craze & soiled and not original – $95.00.

14" "Olga" skating outfit made from the Mary Hoyer patterns. All hard plastic with glued on wig and sleep eyes. Marks: Mary Hoyer inside circle, on back. 1950. 14" Mint – $225.00; Soiled & not original – $95.00.

14" In Hoyer pattern book this outfit is called "Patsy". Coat and hat. 1951. Hard plastic doll with glued on wig and sleep eyes. Marks: Mary Hoyer inside circle, on back. 14" Mint – $225.00; Soiled & not original – $95.00.

HUMMEL DOLLS
HUNGERFORD
ICE CAPADE DOLLS

First prices are for mint dolls. Second for checked, cracked, soiled or not original dolls.

Hummel dolls are made by William Goebel in Germany. The all-rubber dolls were made between 1948 and into the late 1950's, and early 1960's. After 1964 the same molds were used to make the dolls in vinyl. Both material dolls will have deeply modeled hair and painted features. The dolls will be marked on the head, have tagged clothes and will have a paper tag (triangle shaped) attached to wrist or around neck.

12" All rubber and original – $85.00-30.00.

12" All vinyl and original – $75.00-45.00.

16" All rubber and original – $125.00-65.00.

16" All vinyl and original – $145.00-70.00.

16" Hummel boy and girl. All rubber with molded hair and painted features. All original. Courtesy Louise Nixon. $125.00 each.

15" Lastic plastic legs and head with vinyl arms and body. Blue sleep eyes, open mouth/nurser. Cheek dimples and bent baby legs. Marks: Hungerford, on neck. 1956. 15" Mint – $45.00; 15" Soiled, not original – $22.50.

ICE CAPADE DOLLS

All prices are for mint dolls.

For over twenty years the costume department of Ice Capade has been dressing dolls in the exact materials and design planned in using for the skater's costumes.

The reason for this has been to see if the materials and designs are "workable". This process eliminates expensive mistakes. These costumes are hand sewn, in scale to the doll and include every bead, sequin, drape, feather used for the full size costumes.

A few years ago some of the Ice Capade dolls were released to the general collector. The dolls used will be from Italy with adult figures (early 1950's), The Binnie Walkers, Cissy and Jacqueline dolls by Madame Alexander and later the very adult style dolls made by Kaysam. THERE ARE NO NUDE ICE CAPADE DOLLS, and it must be noted that a few nude Kaysam dolls have been advertised as being Ice Capade dolls.

The Italian dolls will be unmarked, the dolls by Madame Alexander will be marked with the Alexander name with the Jacqueline doll also being marked with the year 1961. The Kaysam dolls used will be marked: 4272/K/1961.

Italian dolls: any size: $250.00 up; Kaysam: $375.00 up.

Binnie Walker: $400.00 up.

Cissy: $600.00 up.

Jacqueline: $900.00 up.

18″ "Parisian Precision" from the 1958-59 Ice Capades. This doll is one made by Furga, Italy and the doll is all rigid plastic with sleep eyes. Courtesy Marlowe Cooper. $250.00.

21″ Doll called "Reflections" and used in the opening number of the 34th Ice Capades in 1975. The doll is plastic, vinyl and marked: Kaysam 1961. Courtesy Marlow Cooper. $375.00 up.

ICE CAPADE DOLLS

24″ "Zodiac" from the 1968 Ice Capades. The doll is plastic and vinyl and marked: 4373/K/1961, on the head. Courtesy Marlowe Cooper. $375.00 up.

20″ Cissy used for the Ice Capade number "Cavalcade of Hits" 1959-1960. Wig has been removed and replaced with head piece of sequines and feathers by the design department of Ice Capades. Courtesy Marlowe Cooper. $600.00 up.

20″ "Gypsy" with removable skirt, gold coin trim, skates attached to leather boots. Doll by Kaysam (Jolly Toys). From the 1972 number called "Gypsy". Doll is marked: 4272/K/1961, on head. Courtesy Marlowe Cooper. $375.00 up.

IDEAL NOVELTY AND TOY COMPANY

First prices are for mint dolls. Second for crazed, soiled, dirty or not original.

Baby Belly Button: Plastic/vinyl. 9″ White – $8.00-4.00; Black – $15.00-8.00.

Baby Big Eyes: Vinyl coated cloth/vinyl: 21″ – $45.00-20.00.

Baby Crissy: 24″ White – $35.00-15.00; Black – $45.00-20.00.

Baby Snooks and other "flexie": Wire and composition: 12″ – $225.00-95.00.

Bam Bam: Plastic/vinyl or all vinyl: 12″ – $10.00-4.00; 16″ – $15.00-9.00.

Batgirl and other Super Women: Vinyl: 12″ – $65.00-20.00.

Betsy McCall: Hard plastic/vinyl head: 14″ – $125.00-40.00.

Betsy Wetsy: Hard plastic/vinyl: 12″ – $30.00-12.00; 14″ – $40.00-18.00.

All vinyl: 12″ – $20.00-8.00; 18″ – $60.00-25.00.

Betty Big Girl: Plastic/vinyl: 30″ – $125.00-60.00.

Bizzy Lizzy: Plastic/vinyl: 17″ – $28.00-14.00.

Blessed Event: Called "Kiss Me". Cloth body with plunger in back to make doll cry or pout. Vinyl head with eyes almost squinted closed: 21″ – $65.00-30.00.

Bonnie Braids: Hard plastic/vinyl head: 13″ – $42.50-15.00.

Brandi of Crissy Family: 18″ – $50.00-25.00.

Brother/Baby Coos: Composition head/laytex: 24″ – $25.00-15.00.

Hard plastic head/vinyl: 24″ – $45.00-22.00.

Bye Bye Baby: Lifelike modeling: 12″ – $90.00-40.00; 25″ – $225.00-100.00.

Cinnamon of Crissy Family: 12″ – $50.00-25.00; Black – $90.00-40.00.

Cricket of Crissy Family: 18″ – $25.00-15.00; Black – $55.00-25.00; Look-a-Round – $25.00-15.00.

Crissy: 18″ – $25.00-15.00; Black – $55.00-25.00;   Look-a-Round   – $25.00-15.00.

Daddy's Girl: 42″ – $750.00-250.00.

Deanna Durbin: All composition: 17″ – $300.00-125.00; 21″ – $425.00-175.00.

Dianna Ross: Plastic/vinyl: 18″ – $135.00-75.00.

Dina of Crissy Family: 15″ – $50.00-25.00.

Flossie Flirt: Cloth/composition. Flirty eyes: 22″ – $95.00-40.00.

Giggles: Plastic/vinyl: 16″ – $35.00-18.00; 18″ – $50.00-25.00.

Goody Two Shoes: 18″ – $50.00-20.00; Walking/talking: 27″ – $85.00-40.00.

Harriet Hubbard Ayers: Hard plastic/vinyl head: 14½″ – $95.00-35.00; 18″ – $125.00-50.00.

Judy Garland: All composition: 14″ – $750.00-250.00; 18″ – $950.00-300.00.

Marked with backward 21: 18″ – $250.00-95.00.

Kerry of Crissy Family: 18″ – $40.00-20.00.

King Little: Composition and wood: 14″ – $145.00-70.00.

Kissy: 22″ – $40.00-20.00; Black – $100.00-50.00.

Kissy, Tiny: 16″ – $45.00; 22″ – $60.00-30.00; Black – $100.00-50.00.

Little Lost Baby: Three-faced doll: 22″ – $40.00-18.00.

Magic Lips: Vinyl coated cloth/vinyl. Lower teeth: 24″ – $55.00-30.00.

Mama Dolls: Composition/cloth: 18″ – $50.00-22.00; 23″ – $75.00-35.00.

Hard plastic/cloth: 18″ – $40.00-20.00; 23″ – $55.00-25.00.

Mary Hartline: All hard plastic: 15″ – $125.00-60.00; 21″ – $175.00-85.00.

Mia of Crissy Family: 15½″ – $35.00-18.00.

Miss Curity: Hard plastic: 14″ – $125.00-60.00.

Miss Ideal: Multi-jointed: 25″ – $85.00-35.00; 28″ – $125.00-60.00.

Miss Revlon: 10½″ – $45.00-18.00; 17″ – $60.00-28.00; 20″ – $80.00-40.00.

Mitzi: Teen type: 12″ – $40.00-18.00.

Patti Playpal: 30″ – $125.00-60.00; 36″ – $150.00-70.00.

Pebbles: Plastic/vinyl & all vinyl: 8″ – $12.00-5.00; 12″ – $15.00-8.00; 15″ – $20.00-10.00.

Penny Playpal: 32″ – $125.00-60.00.

IDEAL NOVELTY AND TOY COMPANY

Peter Playpal: 38″ – $225.00-95.00.
Pinocchio: Composition/wood. 11″ – $175.00-65.00; 21″ – $450.00-125.00.
Sandy McCall: Boy: 36″ – $300.00-150.00.
Sara Ann: Hard plastic, marked P-90. Saran wig: 14″ – $100.00-45.00.
Saralee: Cloth/vinyl. Black: 18″ – $125.00-50.00.
Saucy Walker: 16″ – $50.00-20.00; 19″ – $75.00-30.00; 22″ – $85.00-40.00. Black: 22″ – $145.00-70.00.
Shirley Temple: See that section.
Snow White: All composition: 12″ – $385.00; 18″ – $450.00-135.00.
Sparkle Plenty: 15″ – $45.00-20.00.
Tara: Grow hair. Black: 16″ – $25.00-18.00.

Tammy: 9″ – $20.00-12.00; Black – $35.00-15.00; Grown-up: 12″ – $20.00-10.00.
Thumbelina: Kissing. 10½″ – $12.00-6.00.
Tearful. 15″ – $20.00-10.00.
Wake-Up. 17″ – $18.00-9.00; Black – $30.00-15.00.
Tickletoes: Composition/cloth: 15″ – $60.00-28.00; 21″ – $85.00-40.00.
Tippy or Timmy Tumbles: 16″ – $35.00-15.00; Black – $50.00-25.00.
Toni: 14″ – $100.00-45.00; 21″ – $150.00-75.00; Walking – $135.00-60.00.
Tressy of Crissy Family: 18″ – $35.00-20.00; Black – $55.00-25.00.
Velvet of Crissy Family: 16″ – $25.00-15.00; Black – $55.00-25.00; Look-a-round – $25.00-15.00.

25″ & 21″ "Deanna Durbin". All composition and original. White organdy tops attached to velvet skirts and separate printed balero with attached belt. One is dark green and other navy blue. Courtesy Ann Wencel. 21″ – $425.00; 25″ – $600.00.

1940's World War II Soldier. All composition with molded hair and painted features. Cap missing. Marked: Ideal Doll. Courtesy Jeannie Mauldin. $225.00.

IDEAL NOVELTY AND TOY COMPANY

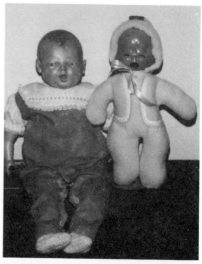

20″ & 14″ Marked: Ideal Doll/Pat. No. 2252077. Hard plastic head and shoulderplate, cloth body with composition limbs. Gifts to owner 1944 & 1945. Later same head used with laytex body. Doll was "Brother Coo's" in 1940's and "Baby Coos" and "Baby Squeezums" in 1950. Courtesy Shirley Merrill. 14″ – $28.00; 20″ – $45.00.

"Baby Snoozie" with early vinyl head and limbs. Cloth body. Eyes are painted and modeling of face is "puckered". Marks: Ideal Doll. Shown with three-faced doll called "Trudy" that is composition and cloth made by Three-In-One Doll Corp. 1947. Courtesy Jeannie Mauldin. Baby – $85.00; Trudy – $125.00.

22″ "Baby Beautiful" of 1945. Cloth body with composition head and limbs. Sleep eyes, open mouth with felt tongue and two upper teeth. Original. Marks: Ideal Doll/Made in U.S.A., on head. Courtesy Edith Evans. $60.00.

20½″ "Miss Curity". Made by Ideal and all composition. Center is 18″ Arranbee's "Sonja Skater" all composition. Both these dolls are original. Right: 19″ "Monica" all composition with human hair rooted into compositon head. Courtesy Turn of Century Antiques. 20″ – $275.00; 18″ – $185.00; 19″ – $185.00.

IDEAL NOVELTY AND TOY COMPANY

16″ "Mary Hartline". All hard plastic. Has heavy eyeshadow and uses the regular marked: Ideal Doll P-90 "Toni" doll. All original. Has "Canada Dry" button with Mary Hartline face, signature and Super Circus printed on it. Courtesy Ann Wencel. $125.00.

21″ "Toni". All hard plastic with nylon hair, sleep eyes and all original with tag. 1949-1952. Marks: P-93 Ideal Doll. Courtesy June Schultz. $150.00.

18″ "Pattie Playpal". All vinyl and marked: Ideal Toy Corp. G-18, on head and back. 1960-1961. Courtesy Shirley Merrill. $75.00.

Two 25″ "Bye-Bye Baby" dolls of plastic and vinyl. Excellent modeling to legs and arms. Courtesy Phyllis Teague. $225.00.

IDEAL NOVELTY AND TOY COMPANY

15" "Carol Brent". Made for Montgomery Wards in 1961. Marks: Ideal Toy Corp./M-15-L, on head. Original dress. Uses the "Tammy's Mom" mold only with dark rooted hair instead of blonde. $35.00.

12" "Tammy Grownup". Plastic and vinyl. All original. Marks: Ideal Toy Corp./B5-12, on head. 1962. $20.00.

20" "Dianna Ross" marked: 1969/Ideal Toy Co. Made during time she was singing with "The Supremes". Plastic and vinyl, rooted hair and all original. Courtesy Angie Landers. $135.00.

IDEAL NOVELTY AND TOY COMPANY

42" "Daddy's Girl". Plastic and vinyl. 1960-1961. Marks: Ideal Toy Corp./G-42-1. Hat added. Courtesy Jeannie Mauldin. Mint – $450.00; 42" – $300.00.

18" "Trilby" or "Little Sister". Three-faced doll made of early vinyl with cloth body. Three tufts of hair attached to hat. Original clothes. No marks. 1951. Courtesy Jeannie Mauldin. $50.00.

18" "Tubsy". Vinyl and plastic. Battery-operated to make hands splash in water and head bobs from side to side. Drain holes in feet. Marks: 1966/Ideal Toy Corp./B-T-E-18-H79. Courtesy Phyllils Teague. $28.00.

Black and White "Giggles". both original. Both marked: 1966/Ideal Toy Corp./G6-18-H-77, on head. Flirty eyes move from side to side as head tilts when arms are pressed together. Courtesy Ann Wencel. White – $50.00; Black – $100.00.

IDEAL NOVELTY AND TOY COMPANY

18″ "Posie". Vinyl head and gauntlet hands. Heavy rooted eyelashes over painted eyes. Foam covered wire body so it is posable. Original bodysuit. Marks: 1967/Ideal Toy Corp./F-13-P-H-11. $22.00.

18″ "Crissy" close up to show lovely detail to head. Plastic and vinyl with grow hair feature. This particular doll is mint in original box as she came from factory but has one brown eye and one blue eye. $25.00.

8″ "Little Southern Girl". 1983. Marked: Ideal Doll. Sleep eyes and all original. Limited Edition (under 600) made for the Collector's United Annual Down South Gathering. $38.00.

I DREAM OF JEANNIE
KAMAR

18″ Bottle and 6½″ "I Dream of Jeannie" doll. Bottle has latch on side to open. Doll is plastic and vinyl with painted features and rooted hair. Made by Remco in 1977. Courtesy Susan Crowsey. 6½″ – $25.00; With bottle – $45.00.

20″ "I Dream of Jeannie". Plastic and vinyl with sleep eyes and rooted hair. Came in green & rose. Represents Barbara Eden of T.V. series. Head marked: 4/1966/Libby. Box: Sidney Sheldon Productions, Inc. 1966/Libby Majorette Doll Corp/Exclusive Mfg. Courtesy Angie Landers. 20″ – $75.00.

13″ "John F. Kennedy". Vinyl head, hands and shoes. "Wired" so arms and legs can be posed. Sits in rocking chair and reads paper about Jackie and children. Key wind music box plays and rocks chair. Made by Kamar. Courtesy Virginia Jones. 13″ – $85.00.

First prices are for mint dolls. Second for played with & missing original clothes or accessories.

Baby Bundles: 16″ – $16.00-7.00; Black – $20.00-10.00.

Baby Yawnie: Cloth/vinyl. 1974. 15″ – $18.00-9.00.

Big Foot: All rigid vinyl. 13″ – $15.00-7.00.

Butch Cassidy or Sundance Kid: 4″ – $8.00 each-4.00.

Blythe: 1972. Pull strings change eye color and positions: 11½″ – $22.00-10.00.

Charlie Chaplin: All cloth with walking mechanism: 1973. 14″ – $50.00-25.00.

"Dusty" plays golf. Wrist and waist are jointed. Elbows and knees bend. Marks: 1977 G.M.F.G.I. Kenner Prod./Made in Hong Kong. $15.00.

Crumpet. 1970. Plastic/vinyl. 18″ – $20.00-10.00.

Dusty: 11½″ – $15.00-6.00.

Gabbigale. 1972. 18″ – $20.00-10.00; Black – $38.00-15.00.

Garden Gals: 1972. Hand bent to hold watering can. 6½″ – $9.00 each-4.00.

Jenny Jones and Baby. All vinyl. 1973. 9″ Jenny and 2½″ Baby – $15.00-7.00 set.

Skye: Black doll: 11½″ – $18.00-8.00.

Sleep Over Dolly and miniature doll: 17″ – $25.00-10.00; Black: $30.00-12.00.

Star Wars: Large size figures: R2-D2 7½″ – $75.00-25.00; C-3PO 12″ – $75.00-25.00; Darth Vadar: 15″ – $75.00-25.00; Jawa: 8¼″ – $55.00-20.00; Stormtrooper: 12″ – $75.00-25.00; IG-88: 15″ – $95.00-45.00; Han Solo: 12″ – $75.00-25.00; Princess Leia: 11¼″ – $75.00-25.00; Luke Skywalker: 13½″ – $75.00-25.00; Chewbacca: 15″ – $75.00-25.00; Boba Fett: 13¼″ – $85.00-30.00; Obi-Wan Kenobi: 12″ – $80.00-28.00.

Steve Scout: 1974. 9″ – $15.00-6.00; Black – $18.00-9.00.

Sweet Cookie: 18″ – $20.00-9.00.

11½″ "Skye" wrists and waist are jointed and has bendable arms and legs. Marks: 1974 G.M.F.G.I. Cincinnati,Ohio/Kenner Products/45202/Made in Hong Kong. Courtesy Penny Pendlebury. $18.00.

KENNER

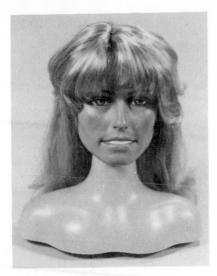

Farrah Fawcett-Majors hair care head. Plastic base and vinyl head with rooted hair. Painted features: Marks: Kenner Prods. 1977/Made in Hong Kong. $12.00.

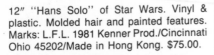

12" "Hans Solo" of Star Wars. Vinyl & plastic. Molded hair and painted features. Marks: L.F.L. 1981 Kenner Prod./Cincinnati Ohio 45202/Made in Hong Kong. $75.00.

15" "Darth Vader" of Star Wars. All plastic with removable cape. Marks: GMFGI 1978/Made in Hong Kong. $75.00.

The K & H marked dolls were made by the Santa Clara (California) Tile Company during World War II. The factory was condemned in 1968 and not torn down until 1973. A quantity of dolls were found in the building and sold to collectors. The basic 7" & 5½" doll was named "Peg of My Heart" and is jointed at the shoulders only. The dolls are painted bisque with glued on wigs and have painted features. They came in boxes marked with both pink and blue dots. The 4" & 5" painted bisque babies marked K & H are jointed at the shoulders and the hips.

7" Girl – $12.00.

4"-5" Baby – $15.00.

5½" Girl – $9.00.

5½" Girl in bottle – $20.00.

K & H "Peg of My Heart" in original box. Has auburn wig, painted-on shoes. Jointed at shoulders only and marked: K & H, on back. Courtesy Linda Lucksinger. $12.00.

5½" K & H in glass bottle. #157 Romona-Early California. In red taffeta dress with black lace trim and veil. Glass jar has incised hearts on sides. Courtesy Linda Lucksinger. $20.00.

4" Painted bisque marked K & H babies. Spray painted hair and painted features. Jointed at shoulders and hips. Courtesy Glorya Woods. $15.00.

KEWPIE

First prices based on mint dolls. Second for soiled, dirty, cracked or crazed & not original. (See front section for bisque Kewpies)

All composition: Jointed shoulders only: 9″ – $65.00-30.00; 14″ – $100.00-48.00.

Jointed hips, neck and shoulders: 9″ – $100.00-50.00; 14″ – $165.00-80.00.

Talcum Powder container: 7″-8″ – $125.00; 60.00.

Celluloid: 2″ – $28.00-12.00; 5″ – $45.00-18.00; 9″ – $100.00; 35.00; Black: 5″ – $55.00-25.00.

Bean Bag Body: 10″ – $22.50-12.00.

Cloth Body, vinyl head and limbs: 16″ – $165.00-70.00.

Kewpie Gal with molded hair/ribbon: 8″ – $25.00-13.00.

Hard plastic: 16″ – $275.00-100.00.

Ragsy: Vinyl one piece/molded clothes with heart on chest. 1964. 8″ – $60.00-28.00; Without heart. 1971. 8″ – $45.00-19.00.

Thinker. One-piece vinyl sitting down: 4″ – $9.00-4.00.

Vinyl, jointed shoulders and hips: 9″ – $45.00-20.00; 14″ – $95.00-40.00.

Not jointed. 14″ – $40.00-20.00.

Black: 14″ – $65.00-30.00; 27″ – $160.00-75.00.

Wards Anniversary: 8″ – $38.00-15.00.

All cloth: (Made by Kreuger): 12″ – $125.00-70.00; 16″ – $165.00-80.00.

Kewpie baby with hinged joints: 18″ – $85.00-35.00.

12″ Kewpie dressed in red cotton. Marks: Cameo, head and body. Jointed at neck, shoulders and hips. Courtesy Myrtle Worsham. $45.00.

18″ Hinge jointed "Kewpie" that uses the "Miss Peep" body and limbs. Marks: Cameo, on head and body. Courtesy Jeannie Mauldin. $85.00.

15″ "Kewpie". All stuffed vinyl with one-piece body and legs. Jointed at shoulders. The features are painted. Has regular "star" Kewpie hands. Marks: Cameo on head and back. Courtesy Jeannie Mauldin. $135.00 up.

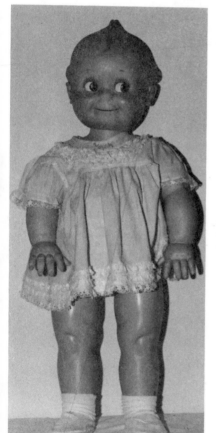

28″ Cameo Kewpie from the 1950's. Heavy weight vinyl head and arms. Not original clothes. Courtesy Kay Moran. $135.00.

"Kewpie Visits Tara". Made exclusively for the Collector's United Gathering Show in Atlanta, GA in 1985. Made by Jesco with original Cameo moulds. $75.00.

KNICKERBOCKER TOY COMPANY

All prices for mint dolls.
Bozo Clown: 14″ – $22.00; 24″ – $38.50.
Clown, cloth: 17″ – $10.00.
Compositon child, right arm bent at elbow: 15″ – $85.00.
Flintstones: 17″ – $45.00 each.
Levi Rag Doll: All cloth. 15″ – $16.00.
Little House on Prairie. 1978. 12″ – $15.00 each.
Lord of Rings: 5″ – $12.00.
Pinocchio: All plush and cloth. 13″ – $48.00.
Scarecrow: Cloth. 23½″ – $45.00.
Seven Dwarfs: Composition. 10″ – $165.00 each.
Sleeping Beauty. All composition with bent right arm. 15″ – $95.00.
Snow White. All composition with bent right arm. 15″ – $95.00.
Soupy Sales. Vinyl, cloth, non-removable clothes. 13″ – $100.00.
Two-headed dolls with vinyl face masks, one crying, other smiling. 12″ – $18.00.
Cinderella with two bodies, one sad face, other with tiara. 16″ – $20.00.

15″ "Sleeping Beauty". All composition with sharply curved right arm, sleep eyes and glued on wig. 1939. Unmarked. Some will be marked: Knickerbocker on backs. $95.00.

13″ "Soupy Sales". Vinyl head with cloth body and non-removable clothes. Marks: 1965 Knickerbocker, on head. Tag: Soupy Sales/1966 Soupy Sales, W.M.C. Courtesy Barbara Coker. $100.00.

12″ "Laura". Marks: Ed Friendly Productions 1978, on head. Has Knickerbocker tag on cloth body. Vinyl head and hands. Represents Melissa Gilbert of "Little House on the Praire". Courtesy Mary Wheatly. $12.00.

258

22″ Unmarked baby with cloth body and composition head and limbs. Sleep brown eyes, molded hair that is painted dark brown. Re-dressed. Courtesy Dorothy Judge. Mint – $50.00; Fair – $12.00.

26″ Unmarked baby. Cloth body with composition head and limbs. Tin sleep eyes, open mouth with four upper teeth. Original clothes. Courtesy Erdeen Wagner. Mint – $65.00; Fair – $8.00.

14″ "Patsy-type". All composition of very good quality and has a Patsy-style body, caracul wig, sleep eyes that are tin and a tiny closed mouth. Unmarked. Courtesy Glorya Woods. Mint – $100.00; Fair – $20.00.

12″ Excellent quality composition with painted features, three tufts of yarn hair on painted black head. Unmarked. Courtesy Jeannie Mauldin. Mint – $35.00; Fair – $8.00.

MAKER UNKNOWN

20" "Dionne-look-a-like" toddler. All composition, molded hair. Re-dressed. Unmarked. Courtesy Evelyn Samec. Mint – $65.00; Fair – $10.00.

16" "Shirley Temple Look-a-Like". Mid-1930's. Open mouth with upper teeth. All composition with a "Patsy"-style body with bent left arm at elbow. May be original. Sleep eyes. Courtesy Turn of Century Antiques. Mint – $95.00; Fair – $20.00.

Unmarked 1920's or early 1930's "Mama" style doll with cloth body and composition head and limbs. Open mouth and sleep eyes. Not original. Courtesy Nancy Lucas. Mint – $95.00; Fair – $15.00.

20″ "Ballerina", sleep eyes with eyeshadow, soft vinyl head, rigid vinyl limbs and plastic body. All original. Has key wind in head wtih music box that plays a melody. Marks: 20, on head. Courtesy Ann Wencel. $25.00.

20″ "Brickette-type" 1960's. Has two-piece body with ball jointed waist. Plastic legs and vinyl arms. Black rooted hair. May have been made for Mollye International Dolls. Courtesy Jayne Allen. Mint – $35.00; Soiled – $10.00.

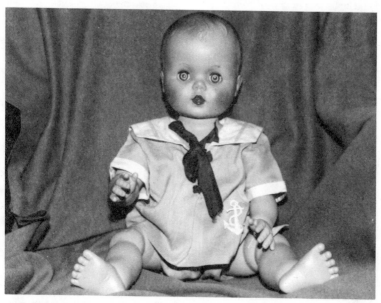

23″ Unmarked boy with vinyl head and limbs and plastic body. Sleep eyes and slightly molded hair. All toes separate. Not original. Courtesy Nancy Catlin. Mint – $25.00; Soiled & not original – $12.00.

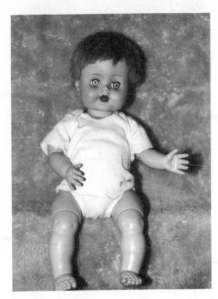

24" Unmarked baby with rooted hair. Vinyl head and limbs with rigid vinyl body. Sleep eyes and jointed just above the knees. Courtesy Shirley Merrill. Mint – $25.00; Soiled – $12.00.

31" Plastic with vinyl head and limbs. Rooted hair, sleep eyes. Original clothes. Unmarked. Courtesy Wendi Miller. Mint – $60.00; Fair – $20.00.

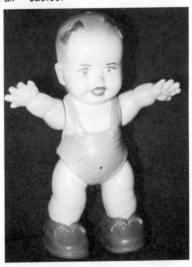

18" "Miss Seventeen". All plastic with inset scull cap, painted features and marked: US Patent 2925784/British Patent 804566/Made in Hong Kong. Box: Louis Marx & Co. 1961. Courtesy Virginia Jones. – $50.00.

6" "Bonnie Braids Walker". All plastic. Had string through stomach to pull so doll would walk. Marks: Marx/Toys/Made in Hong Kong, in circle. 1952. – $12.00.

First prices are for mint dolls only. Second for dolls with clothes soiled, dirty & not original.

Allen: 12″ – $28.00-8.00.

Baby First Step: 18″ – $25.00-10.00; Talking – $35.00-12.00.

Baby Go Bye Bye: 12″ – $15.00-6.00.

Baby's Hungry: 17″ – $22.00-8.00.

Baby Pataburp: 13″ – $15.00-6.00.

Baby See N' Say: 17″ – $17.00-8.00.

Baby Secret: 18″ – $20.00-10.00.

Baby Small Talk: 11″ – $9.00-4.00; Black – $16.00-8.00.

Baby Tenderlove, Newborn: 13″ – $8.00-4.00.

Baby Walk N' Play: 11″ – $15.00-6.00.

Baby Walk N' See: 18″ – $18.00-9.00.

Barbie: #1. 11½″ Mint In Box: $750.00 up; Doll Only: $450.00-100.00.

#2. Same as #1 but no holes in feet – $1,000.00-200.00.

#3. 1960 (still marked 1958 on body) – $65.00-30.00.

#4. Soft, heavy material of new body does not turn light colored. Marked with Pat. Pend. mark. 1961 – $60.00-20.00.

#5. Same as #4 but has one row of hair pulled through for bangs and bangs have a firm texture – $40.00-15.00.

#6. First Bubblecut – $40.00-15.00.

#7. Hard hollow Pat. Pend. body. Rest as #6 – $30.00-10.00.

#8 & #9. 1962 and basically same as #7 – $25.00-8.00.

#10. Bubble cut with paler nails and lips. Midge marked body – $20.00-8.00.

#11. Fashion Queen with molded hair/band, plus wigs – $165.00-60.00.

#12. Swirl bangs (across forehead and to the side). Midge-marked body – $80.00-30.00.

#13. Miss Barbie with sleep eyes. Midge-marked body – $450.00-75.00.

#14. Side part with head band – $300.00-100.00.

Barbie items: Car-roadster – $265.00-80.00; Sports car – $125.00-60.00; Clock – $30.00-5.00; Family House – $45.00-10.00; Airplane – $200.00 up-75.00; Wardrobe – $35.00-10.00; #1 Barbie stand: (round with two prongs) – $50.00-10.00.

Bozo: 18″ – $18.00-8.00.

Buffie: 10″ – $20.00-12.00; 6″ – $12.00-4.00.

Capt. Lazer: 12½″ – $22.00-10.00;

Casper the Ghost: 16″ – $28.00-12.00.

Charming Chatty: 25″ – $50.00-20.00.

Chatty Brother, Tiny: 15″ – $18.00-9.00; Baby – $18.00-9.00.

Chatty Cathy: 20″ – $28.00-10.00; Brunette/brown eyes – $38.00-12.00; Black – $75.00-30.00.

Cheerleader: 13″ – $12.00-6.00.

Cheerful Tearful: 13″ – $15.00-7.00; Tiny: 6½″ – $10.00-5.00.

Cynthia: 20″ – $22.00-10.00.

Dancerina: 24″ – $20.00-8.00; Black – $35.00-15.00; Baby, not battery-operated – $18.00-9.00; Black – $27.00-10.00.

Dick Van Dyke: 25″ – $48.00-20.00.

Francie: 11½″ – $22.00-9.00; Black – $85.00-30.00.

Grandma Beans: 11″ – $14.00-6.00.

Hi Dottie: 17″ – $16.00-7.00.

Herman Munster: 16″ – $22.00-10.00.

Hush Lil' Baby: 15″ – $12.00-4.00.

Lil Big Guy: 13″ – $8.00-4.00.

Kiddles: Mint in packages – $15.00-8.00.

Storybook with accessories – $30.00-12.00.

Jewelry – $9.00-3.00.

Ken: Flocked hair – $35.00-10.00; Molded hair – $30.00-8.00.

Midge: 11½″ – $22.00-10.00; Molded hair – $28.00-12.00.

Moon Mystic: 11½″ – $85.00-35.00.

Mother Goose: 20″ – $35.00-17.00.

Mrs. Beasley, talking: 16″ – $20.00-10.00.

Peachy & Her Puppets: 17″ – $18.00-9.00.

Randy Reader: 19″ – $22.00-10.00.

Real Sister: 14″ – $20.00-10.00.

Rockflowers: 6½″ – $12.00 each-6.00.

Rose Bud Babies: 4″ – $16.00-8.00; 7″ – $22.00-10.00.

MATTEL

Saucy: 16″ – $45.00-20.00; Black – $75.00-35.00.
Scooba Doo: 21″ – $48.00-20.00.
Skediddles: 4″ – $15.00-8.00.
Shrinking Violet: 15″ – $55.00-18.00.
Singing Chatty: 17″ – $20.00-9.00.
Sister Belle: 17″ – $28.00-9.00.
Skipper: – $20.00-8.00; Black – $85.00-30.00; Grown up – $12.00-5.00.
Skooter: 9½″ – $20.00-10.00.
Sun Spell: 11½″ – $85.00-35.00.
Swingy: 20″ – $20.00-10.00.
Tatters: 10″ – $22.00-10.00.
Teachy Keen: 17″ – $16.00-8.00.
Teener: 4″ – $20.00 each-10.00.
Tinkerbelle: 19″ – $12.00-7.00.
Tippy Toes: 16″ – $18.00-8.00; Tricycle or Horse – $10.00-5.00.
Truley Scrumptious: 11½″ – $55.00-22.00.
Tutti: 6″ – $18.00-9.00; Packaged Sets – $35.00.
Todd: 6″ – $18.00-9.00.
Twiggy: 11″ – $45.00-20.00.

#1 "Barbie". Has inverted "v" eyebrows, eyes have iris painted white and doll has holes in bottom of feet with metal tubes for doll to fit on #1 doll stand. $450.00 up.

Round black stand for the #1 Barbie. The rod fits into the feet of the first Barbies. Courtesy Marie Ernst. $50.00.

Left to right is Ken, Barbie, Midge, Brad and Skipper. All are original. Courtesy Angie Landers. Ken – $35.00; Barbie – $40.00; Midge – $22.00; Brad – $25.00; Skipper – $20.00.

Rare gift set called "Sparkling Pink". Box has Barbie and two pink outfits. Any of these gift pack sets are considered rare. Courtesy Pat Timmons. $185.00 up.

17" "Sister Belle". Hard plastic head, rest is cloth. Shows two dolls with eyes painted in the opposite directions. Both are original. Yarn wigs. Pull string talkers. Courtesy Jeannie Mauldin. $28.00.

MATTEL

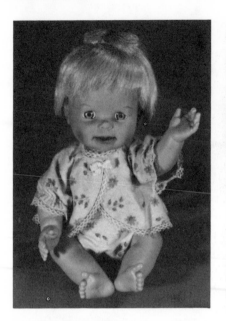 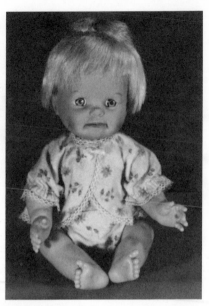

13″ "Cheerful-Tearful". Pull arm down to change face expression. Marks: 1965 Mattel. $28.00.

13″ 1965 Mattel "Cheerful-Tearful". Expression of face changes as arm is moved. $28.00.

4″ "Heather Hiddlehorse Skediddle". Red hair, blue painted eyes and came with horse, tractor and scooter. Marks: 1967/Mattel, Inc. $15.00.

12″ "Baby Go Bye Bye". 1968 Mattel. Painted features, open/closed mouth with two upper teeth. Original. Courtesy Sally Bethscheider. $15.00.

2″ "Apple Blossom". Kiddle Kologne. Green hair, blue painted eyes. Marks: Mattel/1966. $15.00.

16″ "Tippy Toes". Mattel 1967. Original tricycle and horse. Original clothes. Courtesy Jeannie Mauldin. $18.00.

18″ "Swingy" by Mattel. Battery-operated walks, dances and swings. Plastic and vinyl. Original. Courtesy Ann Wencel. $20.00.

MATTEL

18" "Baby First Step". Battery-operated walker. Marks: 1964 Mattel. $25.00.

25" "Charming Chatty" in one of her original outfits. Talks by using record that fits into a slot on the side of the doll. 1961. Mattel. Courtesy Angie Landers. $50.00.

Small "Dancerina". 1968 by Mattel. This small size operates by holding the pink crown and twirling the doll. The large 24" size is battery-operated. Courtesy Angie Landers. $18.00.

268

14″ "Real Sister". Cloth with vinyl head and hands. Painted features. Mark: Mattel, Inc. 1980 Taiwan, on head. Courtesy Shirley Merrill. $20.00.

7″-7½″ "Silvie Rosebud". All vinyl, painted features and rooted hair. Mark: Mattel, Inc. 1976. Also came in 4″ size. Courtesy Shirley Merrill. $22.00.

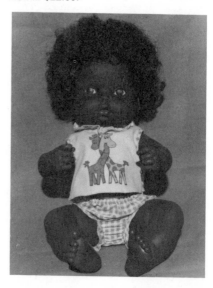

Black and White 17″ "Peaches and her puppets". Pull-string operated. 1972 Mattel. Courtesy Jeannie Mauldin. $18.00.

15″ 1975 "Hush Lil' Baby". Plaster and vinyl. Open mouth/nurser. Battery operated rocks her own cradle, which is cardboard, squirms in your arms and when given a bottle, she is quiet. Courtesy Phyllis Teague. $12.00.

MEGO

Prices are for mint dolls.

Batman action figures: 8″ – $8.00 each.
Cher: 12″ – $12.00; Dressed in Indian outfit – $20.00.
Dianna Ross: 12½″ – $25.00.
Dinah-Mite: 7½″ – $9.00; Black – $12.00.
Happy Days set: Fonzie – $14.00; Others – $9.00.
Joe Namath: 12″ – $48.00.
Our Gang set: Mickey – $22.00; Others – $12.00.
Planet of Apes: 8″ – $9.00 each.
Pirates: 8″ – $15.00 each.
Robin Hood set: 15.00 each.

Sir Lancelot set: 8″ – $15.00 each.
Star Trek set: 8″ – $15.00 each.
Soldiers: 8″ – $9.00 each.
Sonny: 12″ – $12.00.
Starsky & Hutch: $9.00 each; Captain or Huggee-Bear – $15.00 each.
Super Women action figures: 8″ – $8.00 each.
Waltons: 8″ – $9.00 each.
Wizard of Oz: Dorothy 8″ – $15.00; 15″ – $35.00.

Munchkin – $10.00.

Wizard – $12.00.

Others: 8″ – $10.00; 15″ – $35.00 each.

24″ "MS Fashion". Plastic and vinyl with jointed waist. Rooted hair, set blue eyes. Has small waist and large hips. Marks: Hong Kong, on head and lower and upper back. 1973. Courtesy Lita Wilson. $22.00.

8″ "Friar Tuck", "Will Scarlet" and "Little John". All action figures and all original. Marks: Mego Corp./Reg. U.S. Pat. Off./Patent Pending/Hong Kong/MCMLXXi. 1975. $20.00 each.

8″ "Cornelius and Zira" of the Planet of the Apes. Jointed full action figures. Marks: AP-JAC Productions/20th Century Fox Films Corp. $9.00 each.

12½″ "Arcturian" from the Star Trek Series. Fully jointed action figure. Marks: Mego Corp. Courtesy Renie Culp. $15.00.

MOLLYE

Prices are for mint dolls.

Mollye Goodman of International Doll Co. and Hollywood Cinema Fashions of Philadelphia, PA, made dolls in cloth, composition, hard plastic and vinyl. Only the vinyl dolls may be marked with her name on the heads, the remainder will usually have a paper tag. She purchased undressed, unmarked dolls from various companies and designed clothes for them and they were sold under her name.

Airlines. Hard plastic: 14″ – $125.00; 18″ – $165.00; 23″ – $200.00; 28″ – $250.00.

Babies: All composition: 15″ – $95.00; 21″ – $125.00.

Composition/cloth: 18″ – $18.00 – $65.00; 23″ – $95.00.

All hard plastic: 14″ – $60.00; 20″ – $100.00.

Hard plastic/cloth: 17″ – $65.00; 23″ – $95.00.

Vinyl: 10″ – $20.00; 15″ – $30.00.

Cloth: Children: 15″ – $95.00; 18″ – $110.00; 24″ – $135.00; 29″ – $175.00.

Young ladies: 16″ – $120.00; 21″ – $175.00.

Internationals: 13″ – $65.00; 15″ – $95.00; 27″ – $125.00.

Composition: Children: 15″ – $85.00; 18″ – $125.00.

Young ladies: 16″ – $160.00; 21″ – $250.00.

Jeanette McDonald: 27″ – $450.00 up.

Bagdad dolls: 14″ – $175.00; 19″ – $325.00.

Sultan: 19″ – $385.00.

Sabu: 15″ – $385.00.

Vinyl children: 8″ – $18.00; 11″ – $25.00; 16″ – $40.00.

MOLLYE

The entire grouping of the dolls from the film "Thief of Bagdad" made by Mollye Goldman of International Dolls and Hollywood Cinama Fashions. $175.00 up each.

15" International. All cloth. Extremely well designed and made clothing. Has paper tag tied to wrist. Mask face and yarn hair. $95.00.

18" "Queen Elizabeth". All hard plastic. 1953-1954. Has train rather than cape. The hairdo is especially well done. $165.00.

272

16" "Monica". All composition with human hair embedded into scalp. Painted features. All original. Marks: none. 16" – $275.00; 21" – $385.00.

18" "Marion". All hard plastic with rooted hair into hard plastic scalp. Sleep eyes. Marks: none. Tag: Monica Doll Hollywood. Original clothes. 18" – $275.00.

NANCY ANN STORYBOOK

The painted bisque Nancy Ann dolls will be marked: Story Book Doll U.S.A. and the hard plastic dolls marked: Storybook Doll U.S.A. Trademark Reg. The only identity as to whom the doll represents is a tiny wrist tag with the doll's name on it. The boxes are marked with name of doll, but many of these dolls are found in the wrong boxes.

Bisque: 5" – $40.00; 7½"-8" – $45.00; Black – $75.00.
Plastic: 5" – $32.00; 7½"-8" – $35.00; Black – $60.00.

Bisque bent leg baby: 3½"-4½" – $50.00.
Plastic bent leg baby: 3½"-4½" – $40.00.
Marked: Nancy Ann. All vinyl: 10½" – $45.00 up.
Muffie. All hard plastic: 8" Dress – $85.00; Ballgown – $100.00; Riding habit – $125.00.
17"-18" All hard plastic in ballgowns – $225.00.

NANCY ANN STORYBOOK

"Hush a Bye Baby" twin set in oval box that is 9" x 12" x 6". The box is pink with white dots. The twins are 4½" tall and dressed in pink and white. Courtesy Pat Timmons. $50.00 each; Boxed set – $250.00 up.

8" "Muffie" by Nancy Ann Storybook dolls. All hard plastic with sleep eyes and shown with her original box. Courtesy Jay Minter. $85.00 up.

First prices are for mint dolls. Second for played with, soiled, dirty & no clothes.

Designed by Johnny B. Gruelle in 1915 and is still being made. **Early dolls** by Johnny B. Gruelle wil have black stamp on front "Patented Sept. 7, 1915. All cloth, brown yarn hair, tin button eyes (or wooden), painted lashes below eyes and no outline to white of eyes. Some are jointed by having the knees or the elbows sewn. Features on early dolls are painted on cloth. 15"-16" – $285.00-75.00; 23"-24" – $350.00-85.00.

Averill, Georgene dolls. Red yarn hair, printed features and have cloth label sewn to side seam of body. Mid-1930's to 1963. 15" – $45.00-20.00.

Mollye Dolls: Red yarn hair and printed features. Will be marked in printed writing on front upper torso "Raggedy Ann and Raggedy Andy Dolls/Manufactured by Mollye Doll Outfitters". 15"-16" – $125.00-80.00; 22"-24" – $195.00-95.00. **Knickerbocker Toy Co.** dolls: Printed features, red yarn hair. Will have tag sewn to seam with name of maker. 1963 to 1982. 12" – $12.00-6.00; 17" – $20.00-10.00; 24" – $30.00-15.00; 26" – $42.00-20.00. **Vinyl dolls:** 8½" – $9.00-3.00; 12" – $12.00-6.00; 16" – $17.00-8.00; 20" – $22.00-10.00.

Applause dolls: Will have tag sewn in seam. These dolls are still available.

Older 19" "Raggedy Ann" with tin button eyes. $125.00.

8½" "Raggedy Ann". All vinyl and jointed only at neck. Marks: Hobbs Merrill Co., Inc. 1965. Courtesy Wendi Miller. $9.00.

RAGGEDY ANN AND ANDY
REMCO

8½" Red yarn hair and has molded on white cloth with removable navy blue jumper and suspender pants. Set in black plastic eyes. Marks: Royalty Ind. of Fla. Inc. 1974, on back and sole of foot. Courtesy Jeanne Mauldin. $6.00 each.

24" "Raggedy Ann & Andy". Rooted yarn hair in vinyl heads, plastic bodies, original. Marks: The Hobbs-Merrill Inc./1973. Courtesy Marie Ernst. $30.00 each.

REMCO

First prices are for mint dolls. Second for soiled, dirty & not original dolls.

Adams Family figures: 5½" – $9.00 each-3.00 each.

Baby Crawlalong: 20" – $18.00-6.00.

Baby Grow a Tooth: 14" – $24.00-8.00; Black – $35.00-12.00.

Baby Know It All. 1969: 17" – $18.00-6.00.

Baby Laugh a Lot: 16" – $15.00-7.00; Black – $30.00-15.00.

Baby Sad & Glad: 14" – $20.00-12.00.

Dave Clark 5: 4½" – $45.00; set-20.00 set.

Heidi: 5½" – $8.00-3.00; Herby: 4½" – $10.00-4.00; Spunky (glasses): 5½" – $12.00-4.00.

Jeannie, I Dream of: 6" – $10.00-4.00.

Jumpsy: 14" – $15.00-6.00; Black – $22.00-10.00.

Laurie Partridge: 19" – $45.00-15.00.

L.B.J. portrait: 5½" – $22.00-8.00.

Little Chap Family: set of four – $150.00-50.00; Dr. John: 14½" – $40.00-15.00; Lisa, 13½" – $35.00-10.00; Libby, 10½" – $25.00-8.00; Judy, 12" – $25.00-8.00.

Mimi. Battery operated singer: 19" – $35.00-12.00; Black – $60.00-20.00.

Orphan Annie. Plastic & vinyl. 15" – $35.00-14.00.

Tumbling Tomboy. 1969: 16" – $15.00-6.00.

Rainbow & Computer. 1979: 8½" – $25.00-8.00.

276

6″ "Winkin' Heidi". Plastic and vinyl, sleep eyes and has button in chest to make her wink. Marks: Remco, Inc./1968. $9.00.

19″ "Laurie Partridge" from T.V. series "The Partridge Family" and played by Susan Dey. Marks: 1973/Remco Ind. Inc./Harrison NJ/-Item No. 3461, on back. Hong Kong/Remco Inc/1973, on head. $45.00.

18″ "Ginger Snap" & 7″ "Kewpie". For two short years Remco had the rights to make Kewpie. Marks: Doll-E4/Remco Ind. Inc./1968, on head. Kewpie: 7A/JLK/2/ Cameo, on head. Kewpie, on foot and Cameo, on back. $45.00.

7″ "Ronald McDonald". Rigid plastic head and body, vinyl limbs. Button in back moves head. Painted features. Marks: 1976 McDonalds/System Inc./Remco 1978/Made in Hong Kong. Courtesy Mrs. Frank Miller. $7.00.

REMCO
ROYAL DOLLS

14" "Baby This N That". Squeeze feet and doll holds phone or spoon up-arms raise up as if using. Original sunsuit, plastic tight fitting shoes. 1976 by Remco. Courtesy Phyllis Teague. $16.00.

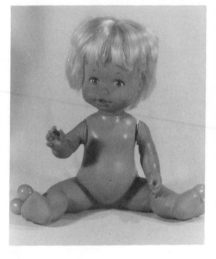

Shows a nude "Baby This N That". Marks: Remco 1976/N.Y.N.Y. 10015, on head. Remco Toys Inc./New York/N.Y. 10010/Made in Hong Kong/Patent Pending/Pro. on body. Two types vinyl on head with skull cap for rooted hair. Two large toes. Two styles of jointing of shoulders. $16.00.

11" "Joy". All vinyl with rooted hair, painted eyes and marked: A Royal Doll/'65, on head. 1965/A Royal Doll, on back. Original. $25.00.

Prices are for mint dolls.
Billy Joe: Sculptured hair, two upper teeth, latex body – $45.00.
Boy: Molded red hair/latex body. 20″ – $35.00; 27″ – $50.00.
Melissa: Sculptured hair: 20″ – $85.00.

Peter Pan: Red molded hair: 20″ – $45.00.
Sister or Brother. Unusual faces. 16″ – $50.00 each.
Tuffy. Protruding lower lip: 20″-21″ – $28.00.

27″ "Peter Pan" (also used for other dolls). Latex body and limbs with stuffed vinyl head. Sleep eyes and light cheek dimples. Marks: Sayco/18-1, on head. 1953-56. $45.00.

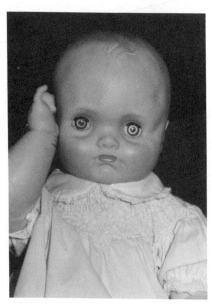

22″ All stuffed vinyl with one-piece body and legs. Molded hair and sleep eyes with very pouty mouth. Marks: Sayco/Doll Corp./-NYC/6U, on head. $38.00.

SASHA DOLLS. These are older Sasha dolls, but since they have not changed the molds at all through the years, the only prices available would be the CURRENT MARKET PRICE of Sasha dolls.

1981 Limited Edition in navy blue velvet dress. Marks: #763, on head (or any other number from 1 to 5000). 16″ – $200.00.

SHINDANA

Prices are for mint dolls.
Dolls will be marked: Div. of Operation Bootstraps, Inc. U.S.A./(year)/Shindana.

Shindana is no longer in business, but was the economic arm of Operation Bootstraps, a non-profit self-help business organization, whose goals were to establish businesses in the riot torn Watts (Los Angeles, Ca.) area right after 1968.

Baby Jamie. Platic & vinyl. 1968: 13" – $22.00.

Dr. J. (Julius Erving). Full action figure. 1977: 9½" – $12.00.

Flip Wilson/Geraldine. All cloth, talker. 1970: 16" – $18.00.

J.J. all cloth talker. (Jimmy Walker). 15" – $15.00; 23" – $20.00.

Kim. Young lady in ballgown. 1969-1973: 16" – $28.00.

Lea. Cloth/vinyl face mask & gauntlet hands. 1973: 11" – $18.00.

Malaika. 1969 young lady: 15" – $17.00.

O.J. Simpson. Full action figure: 9½" – $12.00.

Rodney Allen Rippy. 1979 all cloth talker: 16¾" – $20.00.

Tamu. Cloth/vinyl talker. 1969: 15" – $20.00.

Wanda. 11½": Nurse – $18.00; Ballerina – $15.00; Disco – $15.00; Airline Stewardess – $18.00.

Zuri. Sculptured hair baby. All vinyl. 1972: 11½" – $20.00.

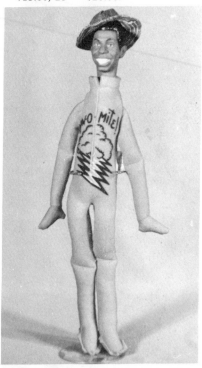

15" "J.J." from T.V. show "Good Times" and played by Jimmy Walker. Removable hat only. Tag: 1975/Tandem Products Inc./Shindana Toys. Vinyl head marked: 1975/Shindana Toys. Body and limbs are cloth. $15.00.

11½" "Disco Wanda" came in two shades, brown and dark brown. Left doll is all original. Right doll dressed in "South o' the Border" outfit for Marie Osmond doll. Marks: Hong Kong, on backs. Courtesy Renie Culp. $15.00.

All composition: Marked on head or body or both. Made by Ideal Toy Company. Must have a Shirley Temple face and hairdo, as Ideal used the marked bodies for other dolls also. **First prices** are for mint and original dolls. **Second price** for doll with light craze, clouded eyes and original clothes. **Third price** is for small cracks, badly crazed dolls and not originally dressed: Allow extra for outfits such as "Little Colonel", "Wee Willie Winkie", "Bluebird", etc.

11″ – $595.00-400.00-85.00.

11″ Cowgirl – $650.00-125.00-85.00.

13″ – $475.00-300.00-85.00.

16″ – $500.00-300.00-95.00.

18″ – $550.00-325.00-95.00.

20″ – $595.00-345.00-100.00.

22″ – $625.00-400.00-120.00.

25″ – $725.00-500.00-130.00.

25″ Cowgirl – $800.00-595.00-150.00.

27″ – $800.00-595.00-175.00.

27″ Cowgirl″ – $875.00-500.00-175.00.

Shirley Display Stand mechanical doll – $1,500.00 up.

Shirley at Organ mechanical doll – $1,500.00 up.

Hawaiian: marked Shirley doll: 18″ – $600.00.

Baby. Marked Shirley Temple on head.

Price scale same as for dolls:

16″ – $550.00-325.00-95.00.

18″ – $625.00-400.00-120.00.

22″ – $700.00-425.00-130.00.

25″ – $785.00-450.00-140.00.

27″ – $825.00-500.00-140.00.

Vinyl of 1950's. Marked Ideal Doll and size number. Has set-in teeth. Allow more for flirty eyes in 17″ and 19″ sizes.

12″ mint in box – $125.00; mint, not in box – $100.00; dirty – $25.00.

15″ mint in box – $200.00; mint, not in box – $175 dirty – $85.00.

17″ mint in box – $250.00; mint, not in box – $225.00; dirty – $95.00.

19″ mint in box – $325.00; mint, not in box – $300.00-dirty – $125.00.

36″ mint in box – $1,400.00; mint, not in box – $1,300.00; dirty – $600.00.

1972 re-issue for Montgomery Wards – $150.00; dirty – $45.00.

1973. Has box with many pictures of Shirley on it. Doll in red polka dot dress: 16″ mint in box – $65.00; Mint, no box – $50.00.

Pin. OLD (1930's) doll pin – $75.00.

Statue: Chalk. In dancing dress, 7″-8″ – $28.00.

Japanese: Mold hair. All composition. 7″-8″ – $165.00.

Group of 22″ Shirley Temple dolls of the 1930's in dancing dresses. Courtesy Glorya Woods. 22″ – $625.00.

SHIRLEY TEMPLE

25″ Shirley is shown with 16″ Shirley baby. They both have flirty eyes. The baby has a cloth body and composition head and limbs. The 25″ is all composition. Both are marked: Shirley Temple. Courtesy Glorya Woods. 25″ – $725.00; 16″ – $550.00.

27″ "Cowgirl/Ranger doll". All composition and original except has replaced hat, gun is missing. Courtesy Joanna Brunken. $875.00 up.

36″ "Shirley Temple". Vinyl with sleep eyes and all original. Still has factory hair pins in hair. Original dress pin. Marks: ST36-38-2, on head. G-36-7, on back. Courtesy Shirley Merrill. $1,300.00.

12″ Re-issued Shirley for Montgomery Wards in 1972. Wears white lightly floral embossed organdy dress with red velveteen jumper style top. Courtesy Mary Williams. $150.00.

13" "Simplicity Pattern Doll". Composition with removable arms. Painted features and shoes with composition dowel-style pins to fit wood stand. 1940's. Shown with original pamphlet. Courtesy Pat Timmons. In box – $85.00.

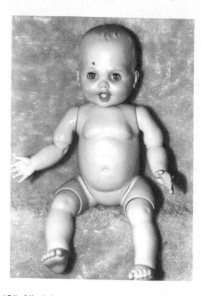

18" All rigid vinyl, molded hair and sleep eyes. Extra joints at elbows and knees. Wide open/closed mouth and rather a pained expression on face. Marks: S20-9. Made by Skippy Doll Co. Courtesy Shirley Merrill. $25.00.

17" Marked: Star Doll, on head. Plastic and vinyl with sleep eyes, rooted hair and may have on original dress. Replaced shoes and socks. Courtesy Jayn Allen. $22.00.

BANNISTER BABY. Doll will be marked: Constance Bannister, New York, New York. She was a famous photographer, especially of children, and the doll was modeled from one of her photographs. Made by the Sun Rubber Company. Sleep eyes and molded hair: 17" early "lastic-plastic". After 1955 heavy vinyl. 17". Courtesy Phyllis Teague. $40.00.

SUN RUBBER

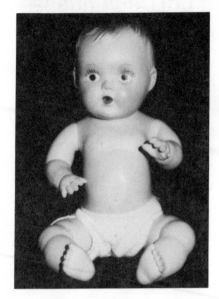

11" "Sunbabe". All rubber with molded hair, painted eyes and open mouth/nurser. Marks: Mfg. by/Sun Rubber Co./Barberton O USA/Pat. 2118682/Pat.2160739. 1950. $28.00.

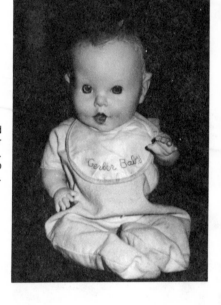

11" "Gerber Baby". All rubber with molded hair and inset eyes. Marks: Gerber Baby/Gerber Products Co., on head. Mfg. By/The Sun Rubber Co./Barberton Ohio USA/Pat #(covered by squeeker in body). 1956. $30.00.

18" Sun Rubber doll that is all vinyl, sleep eyes and rooted hair. Open mouth/nurser. Original clothes. Late 1950's. Marks: Mfg. by/The Sun Rubber Co./Barberton, Ohio U.S.A./Under one or more U.S. Pat. 2118682, 2100739, 2552216/2629131, 2029134, Other/Pat. Pend./13. Courtesy Martha Sweeney. $35.00.

9″ "Hippie". Yarn hair attached with string through holes in top of head. Marks: 1965/Transogram/Company/Inc. Made to represent "Tiny Tim" singer. $9.00.

17″ "Sun-Dee". All vinyl with sleep eyes, open mouth/nurser. Marks: Mfg. by The Sun Rubber Co./Barberton, Ohio USA/Under one or more US Pat./2118682, 2160739, 2552216/2629131, 2629134 Other Pat. Pend., on back. $45.00.

TERRI LEE

First prices are for mint dolls. Second for soiled, poor wig, not original.

Terri Lee: 16″ Composition – $185.00.

Hard plastic. Marked: Pat. Pend. – $145.00-65.00; Others – $125.00-50.00.

Black – $325.00-100.00.

Oriental – $350.00-125.00.

Vinyl – $145.00-35.00.

Talking – $165.00-65.00.

Jerri Lee: 16″ Hard plastic – $175.00-75.00.

Black – $395.00-110.00.

Oriental – $425.00-125.00.

Tiny Terri Lee: 10″ – $110.00-40.00.

Connie Lynn: 19″ – $275.00-90.00.

Gene Autry: 16″ – $500.00 up-125.00.

Linda Baby (Linda Lee): 10″-12″ – $175.00-60.00.

So Sleepy: 9½″ – $125.00-45.00.

Clothes: Ballgowns – $40.00-15.00; Riding outfits – $40.00-15.00; School dresses – $28.00-8.00; Skaters – $40.00-15.00; Coats – $20.00-6.00; Brownie Uniform – $20.00-6.00; Davy Crockett – $40.00-15.00;

TERRI LEE

2 pc. suits (Terri Lee) – $20.00-6.00; 2 pc. suits (Jerri) – $25.00-9.00; Short pant suits (Jerri Lee) – $40.00-15.00.

Mary Jane: Plastic walker Terri Lee look-a-like with long molded eyelids – $95.00-30.00.

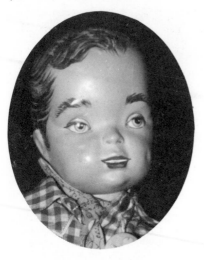

16" "Gene Autry". Same basic doll as the "Terri Lee". Original. $500.00 up.

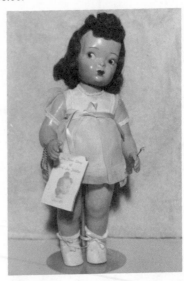

17" "Terri Lee". All composition and completely original. Eyes are painted to the side and are brown. Courtesy Turn of Century Antiques. $185.00 up.

16" "Terri Lee". Rigid hard plastic with glued-on wig. All original clothes, except replaced shoes. Hair is mint in original set. Courtesy Virginia Jones. $145.00 up.

16" "Terri Lee" in one of her original skating outfit. Courtesy Jay Minter. $145.00 up.

10" "Tiny Terri Lee". Walker and head turns. Original, except replaced shoes and socks. Courtesy Jay Minter. $110.00 up.

19" "Connie Lynn". All rigid hard plastic with bent baby legs and glued on caracul wig. Original. Courtesy Jay Minter. $275.00.

10" "Linda Baby". All vinyl with molded hair. Original. Courtesy Jay Minter. $175.00.

TROLLS

Prices are for mint dolls.
Dam Things: 3" – $9.00; 6" – $20.00; 12" – $20.00; 16" – $30.00; 18" – $52.00.
Uneeda: 3" – $7.00; 6" – $11.00.

Cloth body/rest vinyl: 14" – $38.00; 16" – $65.00.
Unmarked: 3" – $5.00; 6" – $8.00; 12" – $12.00.

TROLLS

Animals: Cow – $15.00; Large cow – $35.00; Horse – $35.00; Giraffe – $35.00; Donkey – $35.00; Turtle – $25.00; Monkey – $25.00.
Two-headed troll: 6″ – $16.00; 12″ – $26.00.

Santa Claus Troll: 3″ – $14.00; 6″ – $19.00.
Grandpa & Grandma. 1977: 13″ – $25.00 each.

3″ "Indian Troll". All vinyl with orange hair and inset eyes. Original. Marks: Scanda House/1965/True Troll. $9.00.

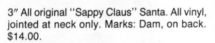

3″ All original "Sappy Claus" Santa. All vinyl, jointed at neck only. Marks: Dam, on back. $14.00.

6″ "Troll Wish-nik" with lavender hair and jointed at the neck only. All vinyl. Marks: Uneeda/Wish-nik TM/Pat. $7.00.

First prices are for mint dolls. Second for soiled, dirty, not original dolls.

Anniversary Doll: 25″ – $48.00-18.00.
Baby Dollikins: 21″ – $28.50-12.00.
Baby Trix: 16″ – $15.00-5.00.
Ballerina: Vinyl. 14″ – $20.00-7.00.
Blabby: $20.00-8.00.
Bare Bottom Baby: 12″ – $14.00-4.00.
Dollikins: 8″ – $10.00-5.00; 11″ – $14.00-6.00; 19″ – $22.00-12.00.
Fairy Princess: 32″ – $65.00-30.00.
Freckles: 32″ – $65.00-30.00.
Freckles Marionette: 30″ – $65.00-30.00.
Lucky Lindy (Lindbergh). Composition. 14″ – $200.00-85.00.
Pollyanna: 10½″ – $28.00-9.00; 17″ – $40.00-15.00; 31″ – $70.00-25.00.
Pri-thilla: 12″ – $18.00-7.00.
Rita Hayworth: Composition: 14″ – $165.00-45.00.
Serenade: Battery-operated talker: 21″ – $28.00-10.00.
Suzette: 10½″ – $20.00-6.00; 11½″ – $25.00-7.00; Sleep eyes. 11½″ – $30.00-9.00.
Tiny Teens: 5″ – $7.00 each-2.00 each.

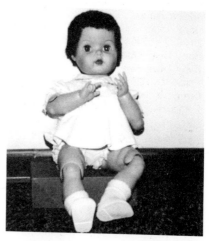

21″ "Baby Dollikin" with vinyl head, rooted hair and large sleep eyes. Dimples and open mouth/nurser. Rigid plastic body and limbs with extra joints at elbows, wrists and knees. Marks: Uneeda Doll Co., Inc., on back. Courtesy Jeannie Mauldin. $28.50.

30″ "Freckles" marionette. Cloth with vinyl hands and head. Rooted red hair, painted features. Mouth is operated by pull-string from back of head. Courtesy Jeannie Mauldin. $65.00.

25″ and 13″ "Vanta Baby". Both have cloth bodies, composition head and limbs, molded hair and sleep eyes. Large one has painted upper and lower teeth and small one upper only. Both marked: Vanta Baby Amberg, on shoulder plates. Courtesy Jeannie Mauldin. 25″ – $175.00; 13″ – $75.00.

VOGUE DOLLS

First prices are for mint dolls. Second is for dirty, soiled, messed up wig, or not original dolls.

Baby Dear: 12" 1961. 17" – $65.00-20.00; 12" 1964 – $35.00-15.00.

Baby Dear One: 25" – $145.00-65.00.

Baby Dear Two: 27" – $165.00-85.00.

Brickette: 22" – $80.00-35.00.

Ginny: (Composition-see "Toddles") 8" Hard plastic. Allow more for special outfits.

Strung. Painted eyes. Mark: Vogue Dolls – $225.00 up-75.00.

Sleep eyes. Painted lashes. Strung: $200.00 up-75.00.

Caracul wig (child, not baby): $250.00 up-85.00.

Painted lashes, sleep eyes, walker. Mark: Ginny/Vogue Dolls: $165.00 up-65.00.

Molded lashes, walker: Ginny mark: $135.00 up-50.00.

Molded lashes, jointed knee walker: $100.00 up-30.00.

Ginny Crib Crowd: Bent leg baby with caracul wig – $250.00 up-85.00.

Ginny Queen: – $450.00 up.

Ginny. All vinyl. Internationals – $22.00-8.00; Others – $28.00-10.00.

Ginny clothes: Ballerina – $25.00; Ballgown – $30.00; Bride – $22.00; Riding habit – $30.00; Skater – $25.00; Prince – $30.00; Hansel/Gretel – $30.00 each; Clown – $30.00; Groom – $30.00; Majorette – $30.00; Skier – $28.00.

Hug-a-Bye Baby: 16" – $22.00-8.00; Black – $28.00-10.00.

Jan: 12" – $35.00-15.00.

Jeff: 10" – $35.00-15.00.

Jill: 10" – $35.00-15.00.

Lil Imp: 11" – $35.00-15.00.

Love Me Linda: 15" – $30.00-12.00.

Star Bright: 18" – $40.00-20.00; Baby: 18" – $40.00-20.00.

Toddles: 8" "Ginny". All composition – $225.00 up-85.00.

Welcome Home Baby: 20" – $50.00-22.00.

Welcome Home Baby Turns Two: 24" – $65.00-28.00.

Wee Imp: 8" Red wig – $200.00 up-85.00.

All composition with painted features. This "Toddles" is dressed in original clothes as Uncle Sam. Has gold Vogue label on front. $225.00 up.

"Ginny" with painted eyes, and all hard plastic. Original dress with felt applied flowers at neck and near hem. Replaced shoes. Courtesy Jay Minter. $225.00 up.

"Ginny" Right: painted lash, non-walker of 1950 "Easter Girl" in lavender with yellow ribbon trim and net at sleeves. Yellow ribbon in hair. Original. Left: Painted lash, non-walker of 1952. #21 Kindergarten series. Side part wig. Embossed organdy dress with black ribbon inserts. Flower in hair. Courtesy Margaret Mandel. $200.00 up.

Early "Ginny" that is strung, has painted lashes and is a non-walker. In original ballgown and hat. Courtesy Jay Minter. $225.00 up.

Poodle Cut Ginnys. 1952. Painted lashes, non-walkers. Left: #40 "Tiny Miss Series", center: #29 "Kindergarten Series" and right: #41 "Tiny Miss Series". Courtesy Margaret Mandel. $250.00 up.

VOGUE DOLLS

"Ginny" with sleep eyes and painted lashes. Jointed knee walker. In original clothes, but hat is missing. Courtesy Marge Meisinger. $100.00 up.

Ginny Gym Set. Made of wood and scaled for 8″ Ginny dolls. Courtesy Marianne McCabe. $125.00.

3 Vinyl ''Ginny'' of Faraway Lands. Dutch girl, Tyrolean and Poland. Sleep eyes and rooted hair. Courtesy Marge Meisinger. $22.00 up.

14½'' ''Littlest Angel''. Plastic and vinyl with sleep eyes and rooted hair. Original except socks are missing. Marks: Vogue Doll 1965, on head. $22.00.

14'' ''Baby Wide Eyes'' 1975 dolls. All vinyl, rooted hair, sleep eyes and open mouths. All original. Marks: Vogue 1975, on head and backs. Courtesy Jeannie Mauldin. White – $18.00; Black – $22.00.

WOOD DOLLS

10″ Carved wood head baby with very soft cloth body and limbs. Painted features. Unmarked. Courtesy Pearl Clasby. $18.00.

10″ All wood jointed at knees, hips and shoulders. Has designed on underclothes, painted features and shoes and socks. Unmarked. Courtesy Turn of Century Antiques. $22.00.

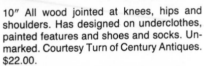

Shows original basic cotton dress that came with wooden, jointed doll. Courtesy Turn of Century Antiques. $22.00.

Two Important Tools For The
Astute Antique Dealer, Collector and Investor

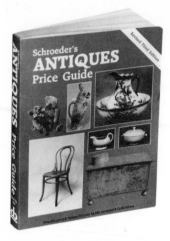